Neijia Yoga

Nei Gong for Yoga and the Martial Arts

William Bodri

Top Shape Publishing LLC
1135 Terminal Way Suite 209
Reno, NV 89502

ISBN: 978-0-9998330-7-0
Library of Congress Control Number: 2020947816

DEDICATION

Yoga and the martial arts each have a multi-thousand year history. What has become lost over this time is an important emphasis on internal energy cultivation for health, longevity, spiritual development and higher physical capabilities. In yoga, inner Qi cultivation is the basis not just for becoming more flexible and agile, but for attaining the liberation of spiritual enlightenment. In the martial arts it is the basis of more excellent *Wushu* skills such as becoming quicker and more powerful. In Taoism, which gave birth to many martial arts techniques, *neijia* internal energy work is also the fundamental basis behind becoming a spiritual Immortal.

Unfortunately, this profound basis of inner cultivation work on one's Qi has been lost. Such yoga teachings still exist within the *kundalini* yoga traditions, but this syllabus is no longer found in the *Wushu* martial arts schools of Shaolin, Emei and Wudang. This book is dedicated to helping restore internal Qi cultivation knowledge to these schools and their monasteries, and to the entire field of martial arts in general, but especially to the monastic traditions that have traditionally combined martial arts training with inner Qi cultivation in order to help practitioners climb the ladder of spiritual attainments. It will help you learn the essential theory of what to practice and why.

CONTENTS

ACKNOWLEDGMENTS

My good friend Xiao Tao was the one who inspired me to write this book. As I did when much younger, Xiao Tao often travels around China visiting its many monasteries, such as the Shaolin Temple, and has cultivated great relationships with many such institutions. As I see it, the problem with Buddhist and Taoist monastic cultivation in China today is that most practitioners have lost proper guidance as to effective cultivation practice, including the traditions that employ the martial arts in their training regimes. The knowledge base on inner cultivation practices is particularly absent within these monasteries due to having been eliminated during the Cultural Revolution, and it is exceedingly painful for me to see the decline that has therefore happened to the Shaolin, Emei and Wudang traditions. Hence, I wrote this book to do something about it.

Inner Qi cultivation is a topic that few actually write about. Very few authors can be recommended. However, we are greatly indebted to the many books of Yang Jwing-Ming since they have brought the most complete set of inner martial arts Qi teachings to the world. Bradford Tyrey's books on Master Sun Lu-Tang, made possible through interviews with his daughter Madam Sun Jian-Yun, are also highly praised because they provide wonderful insights into *nei-gong* practices for the martial arts. You will also find helpful information in *Qi-gong Empowerment* by Liang Shou-Yu and Wu Wen-Ching, and perhaps my own books might be helpful - *Nyasa Yoga, Buddha Yoga, Arhat Yoga, Bodhisattva Yoga* and *Meditation Case Studies.*

1
SALUTATIONS TO HANUMAN
AND SUN WU-KONG

Salutations to Hanuman and Sun Wu-Kong, Lords of the Martial Arts.

One born from the wind element[1] and one from a stone, they both have origins that symbolize mankind's evolution out of insentient matter. Furthermore, as apes with higher consciousness, each of these Immortals represents the fact that we can use our consciousness to rise above our animal natures via the process of self-cultivation. Both Hanuman and Sun Wu-Kong also attained an ultimate excellence in the martial arts, and their skills demonstrated the finest mind-body attainments. They achieved their excellence through consistent external and internal practices.

By cultivating their mind, body, and internal energy they each achieved the ultimate goal of physical perfection, transcendental mind, and mind-body unity. Daily practice to achieve control of their mental states, their bodies and their internal energy was the root of their success.

I salute these two Heroes, monkeys who represent the fact that we are also animals with consciousness, and who symbolize the raw Qi power within our bodies that can be purified and raised to the divine. Both Hanuman and Sun Wu-Kong represent the great mind-body capabilities that man can

---

[1] The wind element represents energy in Hinduism. Hanuman was born from the wind element while Sun Wu-Kong was born from a stone.

1

achieve through training.

Mastering your mind, body and internal energy entails cultivating yourself through exercises to become able to control them, purify them, coordinate them and combine them into one. If you choose this pursuit then, like these two immortal Champions, you will become able to express yourself more perfectly in life through higher manners and elegant consummate conduct that flows.

Murugan or Kartikeya, the Hindu master of weapons and warfare, trained in multiple skills for immaculate martial abilities. His six heads represent having gained control of the strong pelvic energies ascending through our six-nerved sacrum. The Taoist deity Immortal of the martial arts, Xuanwu Shangdi, through his self-cultivation attained superpowers such as control of the elements that he uses to protect people from enemies. The dharma protector Acala,[2] a Buddhist Wisdom King who appears wrathful and threatening, skillfully destroys the strength of demons with his martial skills. He represents taming and purifying malicious, angry Yang Qi so that its power can be applied to liberation. Weituo Bodhisattva, who attends to monasteries that transmit enlightenment practices, devotes his abilities to protecting the dharma and always supports the cause of righteousness.

I salute all these great ones who have devoted their pursuit of martial skills to much higher noble causes than just developing a warlike nature.

A Shaolin legend states that a different god helps practitioners during each posture of the *Ba Duan Jin* (Eight Silken Movements), and each god therefore mandates specific thoughts, emotions, spiritual precepts and inner Qi movements that you should maintain while performing their physical posture. This actually holds true for all the yoga and martial arts forms that involve inner energy work. I salute all the celestial immortals who have vowed the similar task of invisibly helping practitioners learn internal energy movements for yoga and the martial arts.

As sentient beings we essentially possess only two skills: mental (cognitive) and physical abilities. Human beings should therefore be always working on

---

[2] Also known as Budong Mingwang in Chinese Mahayana Buddhism, or Fudo Myoo in Japan.

developing these two capabilities – those of the body and the mind, and body-mind coordination.

Mentally we should always be working to further develop our cognitive skills. We should always be accumulating new knowledge, increasing our wisdom and understanding of cause and effect principles, developing better ways of thinking and doing, and learning skills that will help us to control our minds, improve our situations, and achieve happiness and contentment.

In addition to developing our minds, we should always be working on cultivating our bodies, which are a genetic inheritance, to a higher degree of health and comfort. We should always be working on developing the fitness and capabilities of our bodies. We should always be striving to improve our degree of health, flexibility and agility, stamina, energy, physical comfort and well-being via diet, exercise, habits and by improving our environment. In particular, we should work at perfecting our physical comfort by attaining optimum health and work at perfecting our sensory-motor skills so that they achieve a state of excellence.

Through this cognitive and physical road of self-improvement to become your highest and best self, people will not just improve their internal and external properties, but also their lives and destinies.

Your personality, values, habits, conduct, life path of destiny, your body and its internal energy – all of these must become purified of defilements and elevated to their highest degree. This is the road of self-cultivation, and the martial arts together with yoga are necessary for this objective.

Mind, body and energy coordination is the aspiration, to unify these three as one. The objective is that you always feel pristinely aware of your mind and the environment, freshly alive and full of life energy. To maintain a constant state of pristine awareness where your mind is sharp, quiet, clean and peaceful; with predominantly positive feelings; where your body always feels blissful and comfortable; and where your movements flow with grace and elegance is the highest goal of beingness.

We all want to enjoy unsurpassed fluidity and grace in our physical movements, in our internal mental-emotional states, in our outward behavior, and in our physical form. We all wish to be able to move our bodies in effortless ways that express ourselves with consummate flexibility, agility, speed, endurance, strength and refinement. To achieve the enjoyment of blissful full expression of our being – being full of energy and feeling fully alive with a subtle bliss that is free of suffering and discomfort – this is what we all seek.

Please bless me all noble Great Ones, who have attained the Tao through the pursuit of martial and physical skills, that I may also reach the same pinnacle of accomplishment through the roads of yoga and the martial arts.

2
CONSCIOUSNESS AND FLOW

To attain control of your consciousness means that you achieve mastery over both your deliberate and automatic mental processes. It means attaining control over your wisdom mind that includes your ability to concentrate and make decisions, manage mind-body coordination, and gain regulatory control over your automatic emotional mind that often gives rise to unbidden turbulence and mental afflictions.

The automatic processes of consciousness are like reflexes that naturally happen only they occur within our minds. They include sensory perceptions and their automatic interpretation as objects we recognize; naturally arising perspectives on circumstances (stereotypes and implicit biases) that automatically arise due to our storehouse of memories; emotional reactions that naturally arise in response to events (such as likes and dislikes or various emotional feelings); steady-state emotional personality tones that are a basic feature of your character which flavor it in certain ways; natural desires such as hunger and thirst; breathing patterns; unwanted mental afflictions, defilements, and irritations that naturally arise within consciousness to interrupt states of focus and concentration (such as negative self-talk or annoyances); natural or habitual responses as well as learned tendencies and attitudes that automatically manage how we react to circumstances, such as how we spontaneously respond to threats after extensive training in the martial arts.

Although automatically triggered by other stimuli, many of these automatic mental responses can be transformed through practice and training. They can be retrained into something much better than what we already have inside our neurons as standard patterns. This is one of the main principles of martial arts, which is to replace natural but ineffective body movements and mental patterns with automatic responses that are optimal for fighting and protection. We can definitely transform our breathing patterns, emotional reactions, structural reflexes, and motor responses to have better patterns than they now have.

Military boot camp training tries to pressure-break your old patterns and remold you by installing new ones, but with yoga and the martial arts the motivation should be inspirational rather than forced. Through personal aspirations alone you can gradually transform your patterns into more optimal ones that move you to the next best version of you. Everything in your mind and body will then readjust as you progress in these efforts.

The basis behind successful training in the martial arts is imprinting new movement patterns, energy patterns and mental responses within our minds so that they become automatic responses. We can discipline our movements to express new abilities, and overwrite our old behavioral patterns with higher models of perfection.

Because we are not insentient, consciousness allows our intellect to engage in thinking with understanding, which is called wisdom. Naturally this requires knowledge that depends on possessing a storehouse of memories. Deliberate consciousness accesses our database of memory knowledge and guides the mind in generating our thinking, decision-making, attention, concentration, and perseverance. It also controls the factor of our willpower, volition, self-will, or intent. In some spiritual schools, will or volition is considered a factor independent of our emotions and reasoning.

The deliberate processes of consciousness – which we normally call thinking, conception, discrimination, reasoning or cognition – operate by referencing our knowledge storehouse of memories that we have built over time, which is our "conditioning" or previous learning. Those memories are stored as networks of neural patterns in the brain whose contents determine how we think, feel and act in situations. By developing new memory patterns through new experiences and the conditioning of repeated training, we can change how we think, behave and even move because we will be referencing new neural patterns. Neural re-patterning can change everything about ourselves, including what we think about ourselves, how we approach life and how we move our bodies. Through the neural re-patterning of learning we can even become able to move our internal energy.

Through the training of consciousness we can learn how to focus and concentrate so that we ignore mental annoyances and distractions; we can form new memories and thereby acquire new knowledge and skills; our intellect can fathom out the scientific rules of cause and effect that we can apply to our reasoning and activities; our wisdom and understanding can be widened, deepened or sharpened; we can gain control of our physical capabilities, internal energy, thought process and emotions; we can learn how to make decisions, inferences or assessments using deductive, inductive and dialectical thought as well as hierarchical conceptual reasoning; our mental perspectives and attitudes can be changed; our personalities can be transformed for the better; our cooperative social skills can improve so that we are better at getting along with others; we can voluntarily choose to perform acts of kindness and compassion for others; we can learn to access and control some autonomic processes; we can visualize our intentions and use imagination to develop mental simulations of future events or activities we must perform to achieve goals; and we can create a better future for ourselves, our families and communities through deliberate activities aimed at creating an improved vision of the future.

Ultimately, our deliberate consciousness can be mastered.

We essentially are just a body with a mind. As living beings, essentially we just have two abilities: cognitive and physical skills. Consciousness controls our thinking and emotional states, which are cognitive abilities. The mind also controls the movement of our body (mind-body coordination) and influences the circulation of our internal energy, which are physical traits. All these factors can be intentionally controlled as well as trained to mastery at states of higher performance. Those are two of the objectives in yoga and the martial arts.

If we train our bodies and minds sufficiently, we can experience happier or more peaceful states of mental and physical "bliss" (comfort) as our natural state. Mentally this means that the mind can become happier and more cheerful, or calmer, more peaceful and free of worries, annoyances or afflictions. Physically it means that the body can become healthier, free of pain, more flexible and agile, and ultimately comfortable whether moving or at rest. In such a state your movements flow naturally with grace and ease and you exhibit true manners.

The ultimate goal of our beingness is "flow," which is a state of lucid and vivid presence in all situations where the mind is empty of unwanted defilements and remains pristinely aware while the physical body is experiencing the bliss of comfort. In flow the mind is quiet, clean and free of unwanted mental annoyances while you feel 100% alive, aware and fully present in the moment. Flow is therefore a state of concentration lacking internal annoyances, turbulence or distractions where your mind can remain absorbed in whatever it is doing. It is a type of mental clarity without interruption.

This is the goal of Zen monks in training. Flow is described as a state of pristinely clear awareness, free of mental distractions such as emotional defilements and negative self-talk, where action and awareness are conjoined and supremely in tune with the task at hand. In flow you can demonstrate the highest skills of performance doing something without seemingly striving, and you move through time and space without worries but in focus. In flow you can become immersed in an activity and perform it skillfully with fluid intelligence, great expertise and elegance. Awareness seizes the moment, and all its glory radiates throughout your being so that it is one of the best feelings in the world.

During a state of flow your mind, body and activity seem merged together as one, which is called "presence," "being centered," "being in the moment," "Be Here Now," or "beingness." It is a peak experience where your mind is perfectly clear, your concentration is free of distractions and annoyances, all your systems are in sync where you feel like you are "in the zone," your breathing and internal energy are operating smoothly in union, and you experience an overall feeling of bliss, health, and freshness where you lose all sense of the self. In this state you feel fully alive and act extremely skillfully or optimally, often without any sense of self-consciousness.

During the state of flow there is an intense and focused concentration on the present moment, which is experienced with vivid lucidity. Spiritual schools call this pristine awareness, the state of presence, pure consciousness or "being in the moment." Spiritual practitioners train for this with meditation and inner Qi exercises to open their Qi channels so that their physical energy optimally circulates throughout their body even into their brain, which can then achieve such clarity.

During the state of flow there is a merging of action and awareness, which spiritual schools call the unity of mind, body and behavior. Flow helps to integrate the self because in this state of clear concentration, where you are so immersed in an activity that nothing else matters, consciousness is unusually well ordered and harmonious. Thoughts, intentions, feelings and the senses are all focused on the same goal so all the aspects feeding the experience of living are in harmony. We might say that concentration is so intense and devotedly focused that there is no space to consider anything irrelevant, which is why the mind is keen and free of distractions or annoyances.

During the state of flow there is a diminishing of reflective self-consciousness, or concentration on the self and its usual loud cogitations. Spiritual schools call this a state of selflessness, a forgetting of the self, the quieting of the I-thought, the abandonment of the self, the annihilation of the self-notion, or the quieting of the ego-mind. The I-thought must always be operating within the background of our consciousness in order for there to be awareness of thoughts and objects, but the elimination of the self-notion means that self-talk becomes quieter than usual rather than that you become an idiot. In other words, your thought-stream grows quiet and self-talk is silenced.

During the state of flow there is a strong sense of personal control or agency over the situation or activity at hand, which means there is a feeling of confidence and expertise in handling whatever you are doing. In the flow state you seem to function optimally in whatever you do, and sometimes it is almost as if you are not thinking since the mind is quiet. Even though you may be presented with a challenge, your skill level seems to match the difficulties of your circumstances and because of your focused mental state of absorption your quality of performance also seems heightened beyond what is typically normal. Spiritual schools call this "exhibiting ultimate competency" or mastering one's skills, such as Chuang Tzu's "dexterous butcher" whose carving skills were so great that he never had to sharpen his knife.

During this state of flow your "being in the moment" and your experience of involvement with an activity feel deeply satisfying and intrinsically rewarding. It is a sort of peak experience of satisfying participation with an activity. It is a state of pure mindfulness where there is absolute union with the activity you are performing. Your mind becomes immersed in a feeling of full involvement, energized focus, and enjoyment in the activity at hand. Spiritual schools call this enjoyment a subtle state of mental bliss, and reaching this is one of the purposes of spiritual cultivation.

During the state of flow, the extreme mental quiet of being in the moment with undistracted concentration can even produce a distortion of temporal experience. In other words, your subjective experience of time may seem altered because your mind is so focused and quiet. You might forget all sense of time during this state, or time might seem to go slower. This happens because of being absorbed in the moment where the self-thought becomes quieted and mental disturbances disappear – the situation seems to flow like a lucid dream and so the passage of time is not mentally measured or noticed.

In essence, flow is characterized by a complete absorption in whatever one does which is so complete that you lose track of time. Your concentration is so clear, vivid and fascinating that with no disturbing thoughts to bother you or deflect you, your experience of time becomes altered.

Once you touch the state of flow, you always want to regain it. Athletes who once experienced it call it one of the "peak experiences" of their life, and work hard in order to try and capture it again. It is one of the best experiences of the world, it is the optimal experience of beingness or life. It is the optimal state of a human being that we train for through virtuous and healthy living along with yoga and the martial arts

In the flow state your mind, body, energy and your activity unify in a state of harmonious functioning. It is an experience of full living beingness where you are intensely engaged in an activity with focus, your mind is quieted (calm and balanced without any annoyances or afflictions), your Qi flows perfectly, and you finally feel you are truly present and fully alive. Life is interesting and fascinating, even intense. In the spiritual schools this mental state of enjoyable concentration is sometimes called a state of *samadhi*.

Sometimes it feels as if there is no mind and no body in this state, meaning that in your mental realm it seems as if the I-thought has disappeared along with the noisy self-talk you normally hear within your head. In that situation there is no trace or sign of your presence to disturb the harmony of quiet pristine consciousness. Thus it is sometimes called an experience of pure consciousness – and yet full comprehension is there because you are still thinking quietly in the background, otherwise your mind would not be able to continue identifying and experiencing a world of qualities.

The body is so comfortable in this state that its existence is often forgotten; it is as if non-existent due to the comfort or bliss. To reach this attainment therefore requires a harmony of internal energy and physical health, so you can only reach this state through devoted physical and mental training. This is why we must turn to yoga (that stretches all our muscles) and the martial arts (that require inner energy work) as well as sports and dance. Without both internal and external physical training you cannot achieve the physical bliss of this state that arises due to optimally functioning muscles and organs experiencing perfect inner Qi circulation.

In other words, internal states of joy and bliss for your mind and body must find their root in the perfection of both your body and mind. You must train and exercise to be able to experience this state.

Flow involves your breathing because your breathing affects your internal energy, and your internal energy must be flowing perfectly at the time you experience flow. This is why runners who reach a perfect cadence can experience flow, or athletes can experience it within the activity of optimal performance. Therefore, to reach the state of flow you must undertake consistent exercises to train and practice your breathing that will in turn make your internal Qi circulation progressively better all the time. If your Qi circulation becomes utmost refined, you don't need to be in a state of athletic exertion to experience flow.

Your internal energy affects your consciousness, and consciousness is the foundation of your deliberate and automatic mind. Thus, both breathing and your internal energy must become coordinated and harmonized for you to experience flow – a purity of consciousness along with an intense feeling of being alive because your Qi has penetrated everything within you and is flowing perfectly without obstructions. While your mental realm will be pristine and uncluttered during the flow state due to a lack of mental afflictions bothering/distracting the conscious experience, you will truly feel alive. This is because your body will feel amazing due to the well-flowing energy that penetrates every nook and cranny of your body to energize every cell and tissue.

This is the meaning of "physical bliss" although its higher octave is the state where the energy flow is so smooth and refined that the body feeling is forgotten entirely. This is when you don't even notice you have a body at all because of its optimal health and inner functioning. In any case, during the state of flow you attain to a unity of mind, body and internal energy that provides you with a feeling of both command (due to your clear concentration) and presence.

For this to occur, layers of mental conditioning that inhibit or unnaturally bias the proper circulation of your Qi must be eliminated or retrained so they do not obstruct your clear functioning. Meditation helps you achieve this. When your mind is peaceful, centered and remains clear while your body is relaxed, your Qi will flow along its most natural patterns and reach a proper balance itself. That is why cultivating a calm mind is one of the principal components of the martial arts and yoga.

Unwholesome or improper mental conditioning and behavioral patterns must be replaced with good ones for your Qi to reach its optimal circulation, just as incorrect martial arts postures and forms must be replaced with optimal ways to stand and move so that power can be expressed fully. Exact positioning is vital for the martial arts and for the proper yoga *asana*s as well.

Average motor-skills can be upgraded to excellence if you repeatedly practice optimal motor-skill patterns, practice visualizing your movements according to the optimal patterns, and through repeated practice create frictionless pathways for your internal energy to flow when executing those patterns. With repeated practice, your movements and Qi flow can become superior, and superior can become second nature.

In the martial arts, the proper patterns of thinking and moving become dominant by implanting and then reinforcing those wholesome roots. This requires learning skill sets correctly and practicing them over and over again so that those behavioral patterns become automatic reflexes.

During training you must learn how to triumph over many personal dysfunctions. Since martial expression in movement depends upon your intentions, cultivating emotional control, mental rectitude (straightness) and inner calmness are key. Once again you must cultivate clarity of mind, or pristine awareness that can focus without easily becoming distracted or bothered by afflictions, and meditation is the practice pathway for this accomplishment. A clear mind of calmness and inner peace gives you an advantage when facing an opponent rather than letting hate or anger overwhelm and blind you into making bad decisions. During a fight you must keep a clear head.

Therefore the highest martial arts ask you to cultivate a crystal clear mind that is alert, quick, but mentally tranquil. Yoga asks this of you as well. Your sensing, feeling and judgment should be objective and accurate, which requires being levelheaded and emotionally balanced. This requires that you have worked on cultivating your inner Qi circulation to a harmonious state because if your Qi is not smooth then your mind cannot be peaceful and clear. For your Qi to become smooth you body's structure must also be properly aligned and your body must be healthy as well. Your Qi channels and pathways must also be cleared of impediments.

With health and calmness in the body due to superior energy flow, there is then steadiness and calmness in the mind, and through that calmness one can taste a bit of the quiet of bliss. Yoga has a similar training requirement that you need to practice pranayama and improve your internal Qi circulation in order to attain *samadhi*, which is a clear mind that is the pinnacle of sustained mental focus and concentration. Whether in yoga or the martial arts, you need to cultivate the optimal flow of Qi throughout your body and especially within its meridian circulatory system. When the Qi flow becomes optimal within your brain, whose Qi channels you can open through meditation practice, then this state of pristine concentration becomes possible.

A peaceful or "empty" mind is not a case of blunted or suppressed thinking but is sharp, flexible, and always giving birth to thoughts. Thoughts are never suppressed to produce mental quiet, calmness or clarity. An empty mind of clear awareness, or mental bliss, is clearly aware of everything going on but the I-thought and inner intent seem quiet because the internal dialogue has disappeared, thus producing a realm of internal clarity and calm that seems more pristine and vivid since it lacks disturbances. The vividness is in part due to better Qi flow within the brain. This is the best sort of mental state, but it is only attained when the circulatory flow of your internal energy becomes smooth and complete, unblocked in every appendage, organ, muscle and bone within your body and especially within the brain. You cannot just cultivate the brain's circulatory patterns to achieve this.

This state of flow, where the mind is quiet and can become absorbed in a subject without agitations, distractions or annoyances, is a state of concentration. But it seems to be more engaging and pristine because of the mental quiet of the concentration, and because of the superior Qi flow energizing the brain. This makes the mental realm more vivid or intense, and sometimes flow is therefore described as the state of "presence," "aliveness," "being in the zone" or "being centered."

This is just beingness – our beingness in possessing consciousness that is the great miracle and treasure of existence. Flow state is the apex of sentience because in this state of clarity and focus without annoyances you experience the "beautiful foolishness of things" without mental defilements distracting you and infringing upon the experience. Thus your mental realm is pristine, clean and pure but still fully open and accepting of all experiences. Consciousness knows the beauty of the universe and a world of qualities in the most blissful, pain-free, suffering-free manner possible.

This is the perfection of *sat-chit-ananda* within Hinduism that we must strive for because you are existent (*sat*), there is a purity of vivid consciousness that seems unruffled, calm and pristinely clear *(chit)*, and your body generates a feeling of subtle bliss (*ananda*) or comfort at that time due to being healthy and having excellent internal energy flow everywhere inside. Because you have refined your vitality, every body cell is happy with the finest, most subtle feeling of happiness or lightness. Since the body does not provide any uncomfortable inputs to the mind it can therefore be entirely ignored or forgotten, yet the mind-body connection and coordination retains a state of optimal excellence. The attainment of this vivid mental realm makes an individual feel like they are their true self, a real man, and truly alive. This is the perfected human being.

Because of the excellence you feel in your mind and body, this is also the "*Shen Xin Ping Heng*" of Chinese culture ("body and mind balanced"), or "mind and body become one (are unified)." At the highest attainment level this is also "no extremities," "body and mind both forgotten," "empty mind, empty body" or "no mind, no body" of Zen. Why? At the highest stage the body's physical bliss progresses from a stage of Qi fullness and excitation where every cell feels happy to a state of equanimity where the thrill has quieted down but there is fullness, and hence your body feels so comfortable and smooth that you can ignore it entirely. It is as if you are only consciousness without a body. Your mind's internal narrative of self-talk disappears, and the excitation of feeling alive or full of subtle joy ascends to reach this more refined state of equanimity.

There are *samadhi* states one can attain through meditation practice where the world seems to disappear because the mind temporarily shuts down or "is abandoned," but these are not the spiritual state of "no mind" or "no mind, no body" or even "no-thought" we are after since they essentially entail annihilation and are useless for existence. This is not the proper sort of mental or physical bliss. This is basically insentience or non-existence.

The simultaneous quieting of the I-thought and your ongoing mental narrative (coarse thought-stream) produces the proper "no mind" or "mind forgotten," while the body is also "forgotten" if it becomes very comfortable. In this stage of peaceful comfort both can be termed non-existent to give us "no mind, no body." They don't disappear as happens during sleep so of course they both exist, but they are functioning at a stage of optimal excellence so that you don't even notice them anymore. With disturbances thus silenced, this can be called a state of pristine awareness or pure consciousness.

This is why the Chinese call this excellence "*Shen Xin Ping Heng*" ("body and mind balanced"). *Shen Xin Ping Heng* means that your body and mind are unified. It means that body and mind have become one, and for this to happen consciousness must be free of afflictions due to a focused mental realm of engagement, which in turn produces an internal blissfulness or quiet.

As to the Indian proposed perfection of *sat, chit, ananda* the Chinese don't mention existence *(sat)* because beingness goes without saying. For the Chinese, mind refers to consciousness *(chit)* that you cultivate to a stage of internal peace or extremely subtle internal joy (bliss) while the body reaches the stage of physical bliss (*ananda*), which is a joy in every cell or comfort so refined and wonderful that all excitations disappear and the body sense is forgotten.

To some this is the *Wuji* state of (mental) non-action, which isn't ever a mental blankness because there is always full conscious awareness, but your mental realm is characterized by non-action. What non-action? You can still differentiate objects so mental processes are still functioning, which is hardly *Wuji*. *Wuji* means a purified mental state that lacks the presence of afflictions and loud internal disturbances such as the self-voice. Basically, the mind still operates but seems empty.

By cultivating both your body and mind you reach *sat, chit, ananda* or *Wuji.* You cannot just cultivate your mind by practicing "emptiness states" to reach this experience, as is the route of the Zen school or Vedanta. You must also cultivate your body *and your internal energy.*

In the martial arts and yoga you should cultivate your body through diet, physical exercise and internal energy activities and thereby adjust it gradually until it reaches an always and ever comfortable state of health and energy. You want your Qi to circulate everywhere freely and smoothly and all your body cells to become filled with the bliss of Qi. They should become filled to the extent they can be forgotten because of the fullness and optimal circulation of energy achieved between everything within you down to the cellular level. You should cultivate your body's structure and energy so well that you don't even notice it anymore because it never bothers you in any way since you cultivated it to the point where it operates perfectly.

The body should become healthy, strong, flexible, and its internal energy should circulate smoothly. Thus your body should eventually achieve the superior Qi flow that a baby originally possesses, which we all lose over time. We should achieve a joy of movement through the training of our muscles, movements and energy, and our bodies should move everywhere with comfort, agility, grace and ease.

This is the attainment of physical "bliss" or *ananda,* and is achieved when your Qi is able to circulate freely *and fully* everywhere inside you reaching all the cells of your body. In professional sports, athletes sometimes achieve a stage of bliss when "being in the zone" where they become absorbed in a state of concentration, their breathing and blood circulation are pushed to a state of prime, their body feels absolutely wonderful brimming with energy, they are expertly accomplishing some task at hand where their skill level matches the difficulty of the challenge, and there is a strong *feeling of being alive.*

Physically speaking, this state of flow is one of the best feelings in the world. Your mind is quiet and clear and there is an enjoyable and almost euphoric feeling due to the fullness of Qi that *you are really alive.*

To experience this physical sensation of aliveness your body's vital energy must circulate so well, your organs and muscles must be optimally functioning, your skeletal structure must be so well-aligned, your blood circulation must function without obstructions, and all your body's cells must be firing with flow. This type of bliss involves a fullness of Qi that invigorates you with a high energy level to produce that feeling of aliveness, which has a subtle tinge of happiness or excitement to it.

As stated, a stage of progress higher than this is to attain to a subtle sense of physical bliss throughout all your Qi channels that is so comfortable, all-pervading and equanimous that you don't even notice your body's presence anymore because its heaviness is gone, so we say the body seems almost forgotten, as if non-existent, and a mental realm of pure presence - quiet, clear lucidity (because thoughts have quieted) - takes center stage.

Through yoga and martial arts cultivation, you can achieve either of these accomplishments. Your physical body can reach an ultimate level of development where it is comfortable and relaxed in all situations, any internal tension points have been dissolved, its internal Qi is balanced and flows smoothly, and it moves in every direction with pain-free natural ease. The sensation of the body can indeed become so comfortable that at times you don't even notice its presence because of the diet, detoxification work, breathing practices, exercise, meditation and *nei-gong* practices you have undertaken.

Although mind and body appear separate they belong to the same continuum of energy that makes up the whole of our being. Your body and mind can "become one" at this stage because when your Qi is flowing smoothly everywhere inside you it is as if you become just one unit of energy, and your awareness can connect with the whole body everywhere. This is mind-body unity. You can have awareness of any area of your body without any patchy lapses. You have to be healthy and have done a lot of flexibility stretching and internal energy work to reach this unified state of body and mind.

This stage of physical emptiness where you can forget the existence of your body is the state of "no extremities" or "no partitions" in the martial arts. Your body is so healthy and its internal Qi flow so natural and smooth without tension, impediments, stagnations, blockages or obstructions that the feeling of the body reaches the blissful stage of almost non-existence. All its parts feel comfortable because their energy is threaded together into a single harmonious whole, just as an ocean has "no extremities" or "no partitions," and there is excellent Qi flow everywhere that produces bliss. When your Qi reaches this stage it might even feel as if your body is transparent or has disappeared.

At the highest stage of physical bliss it is not as if you feel energetic, but as if the body is so light that it doesn't bother you in any way. Movements are graceful and effortless, and often entirely automatic without requiring thinking. We colloquially say that your body has disappeared because it has lost its feeling of heaviness and you can therefore ignore its presence due to the extreme comfort, which is then having "no body" or "body forgotten." This is one of the targets of yoga and martial arts practice.

In this state your body experiences an equanimity that lacks all internal tension because of the superior inner Qi flow through the practiced routes of your muscles and tendons. This type of peaceful comfort is not a stage of rapturous ecstasy or excitement or pounding energy as sometimes occurs within the lower athletic sports state of flow. It is a stage where any bothersome, coarse or heavy sensations of the body disappear due to optimal Qi flow, and the feeling of comfort is higher or more refined than the pounding bliss of a highly energized state of "being in the zone." This stage of bliss is a type of forgetfulness that transcends any surging stage of Qi flow, such as you can achieve from running or competitive sports. That type of flow is extremely pleasurable but less refined.

Basically, when you can ignore your body like this it means that you have attained "physical emptiness." It means you have transformed your body completely and are reaching towards the attainment level of a sage. This, then, is the physical "bliss" (*ananda*) of *sat-chit-ananda*. The mind being quiet and peaceful, this emptiness is the mental aspect of "bliss."

Obviously this attainment is due to excellent inner energy work and physical exercises that have transformed your physical body and its Qi circulation. You can only achieve this through physical exercise together with *neijia* cultivation, meaning inner *nei-gong* exercises. You have to enter the realm of inner martial arts or inner yoga to attain this. Such *nei-gong* exercise, done correctly, will always improve your level of martial arts and yoga.

The ocean is just one entity, and so should you also reach a similar stage in your training where your Qi becomes one wholeness without any parts or segments. When you reach this stage of attainment then you can sense the energy in any part of your body. Your thoughts, will and intent will then be able to instantly affect all the Qi throughout your body or in any single part you select, proving that mind and body truly have become one.

At this stage of Qi cultivation, your mind becomes extremely peaceful and calm (quiet), clear and pure, relaxed and natural because of the smooth internal Qi flow. When you are experiencing peaceful mental equanimity without suffering, worries, irritations, or unruliness, that peace and comfort is a type of mental bliss corresponding to the physical bliss of the body. You're just there in the world doing whatever you want to be doing and experiencing through attention just what you want to be experiencing, and in so doing there are no internal distractions to your focus, heavy pressure from the ego-sense, nor even any troublesome self-talk bothering you. The experience is primarily the experience and nothing more.

In sports flow you feel a happiness within your mind, but true bliss is type of a peacefulness and mental clarity without an overt excitation of thoughts and emotions. It is a state of peacefulness that transcends ordinary happiness, and it is matched by physical sensations of perfect comfort too. In true bliss, any mental or physical excitation seems like an unwanted irritation that intrudes upon the vivid wonder of the moment.

Taoists explain that the purpose of meditation is to help you reach the *Wuji* state, which is the original natural state of the universe before Yin and Yang became distinguished. Buddhism calls this a state of emptiness or the void because it lacks any phenomena or other types of differentiation. The analogy is to attain this state of mental peace and clarity, or pristine pure consciousness, which seems absent of thoughts (mental movements or modifications). In martial arts, a state of mental stillness before you strike an opponent, which is a state they cannot fathom since you show no mental leanings in any direction, is also called the *Wuji* state as well.

As the primal origin of the universe from which All springs, *Wuji* is described as formless, pure, and empty (like space) without phenomena. Therefore the *Wuji* state is stationary, non-moving, peaceful and calm. All forces of Yin and Yang are absent in this state because *Wuji* has not differentiated into any phenomena. In martial arts, yoga, and meditation practice, the analogous equivalent is where your mind is empty (because thoughts have not been generated), and absolutely peaceful and calm. Awareness is there, so mental processes are still operating, but self-talk is gone. When the inner narrative is silenced, this is the mind's natural state.

We can call this state of peaceful presence a state of stable mind, calmness, concentration or even flow. It is a stage of "being centered" where your mind is calm, clear, composed and collected. The mind is unruffled by emotional concerns or spontaneous irritations. Thoughts exist, but are not pressing upon your mind in a loud, afflictive way. Your mind is clean and insubstantial, without worries, where thoughts and intent are forgotten so it is "quiet with nothingness." Instead, a world of qualifies spreads out before you in all its pristine glory, and unaccompanied by any form of mental turbulence. It is reminiscent of the famous Pond Haiku by Matsuo Basho where silence reigns, activity appears, and then there is quiet once again:

> The old pond
> A frog jumps in
> Kerplop!

Sometimes this attainment is referred to as "empty mind" because of the internal mental quiet, but your mind is not completely empty of contents or activity because then you would be either asleep, in a coma, insentient, dead or non-existent. Empty mind means that some aspects of the mental experience are quieted and others still working quite fine like the natural ability to automatically recognize objects. Empty mind is mind in its most natural state of calmness and purity without the loud narrative of self-talk, but it is alert and always open to producing knowing and new Knowledge.

The mind is peaceful but alert, pristine in clarity but lacking disturbances to its focus. In spiritual circles this is sometimes called a state of calm *concentration* because coarse disturbances are absent from the thought-stream. Call this emptiness or call it concentration, the meaning in this case is the same.

Your internal dialogue has quieted in this state and the mind becomes free of afflictions, annoyances, defilements and distractions (including heavy feelings of body discomfort or tension) while enjoying the objects of its attention. Furthermore, it doesn't stick to experiences with entrainment but remains free to flow from new experience to new experience. This is the state of always "experiencing the moment" or "enjoying the moment" rather than becoming enmeshed in thoughts and swept away from the present due to clinging to your thoughts (losing the state of presence by identifying with them) or attaching to the past. You experience the *moment* due to a beauty of vivid mental clarity, mental quiet and lucidity.

In this state your thought process is not loud and overbearing nor filled with turbulence. It neither wanders about nor runs somewhere out of control. Your mind is clear, quiet and clam. It stays focused by ignoring distractions, and it enjoys whatever is within the mental realm of experience. It attains a state of clearness where the contents of the mind freely come and go without stickiness, and it is so clean that we call it empty mind. Cognizance is there, but the thought system seems quiet because distractions other than what the mind puts its attention upon are not present.

It takes much cultivation to reach this as your natural state. This is the mental bliss of *sat, chit, ananda.*

In this state of peace, presence, awareness or pristine clarity, the strong ego-thought we normally sense inside us doesn't dominate. Of course there are still the automatic workings of the mind, but you are not absorbed in the self-notion or coarse thinking. The mind does not forever remain empty of thoughts but always generates thinking and Knowledge. However, it is not overly cluttered or burdened with a network of ego activity that gets in the way of direct experience.

Mental bliss is not a state of no-thought such as deep sleep, or a coma where there is an absence of the normal operational patterns of consciousness, because in those cases your existence is irrelevant. We are talking about always experiencing active consciousness, sentient cognizance, or conscious presence that is the effulgence of a mind creating a clear field of experience with vivid qualities, but without other mental distractions or turbulence being produced at the same time to cloud the mind. This vividly alive awareness is also called lucidity or radiant illumination.

Thus we have Hinduism's *sat-chit-ananda*, or existence, consciousness, and bliss as the ideal of human beingness. And, at optimal functioning within that mind-stream the taint of suffering and affliction within both mind and body are absent, which is peacefulness and physical bliss.

This is an optimal way of experiencing the moment. This is how we should be experiencing life. We normally call *sat, chit, ananda* or "existence, consciousness and bliss" your highest possible state of experiential being, and also say it is "*Shen Xin Ping Heng*" or "body and mind balanced." It is also "body and mind unified." These phrases express the very same objective of optimizing the state of our minds and bodies to become, through training, their very best given the physical equipment and conditions we have.

Since you should always be this way, this should be the natural state of a healthy mind and body, but it takes work to get here. You have to train your body, use techniques to cultivate your Qi, and cultivate your mental temperament and habits. This stage can only be attained through the cultivation work of yoga, martial arts and spiritual cultivation. The highest stages of yoga and the martial arts require that you practice the breathing and *neijia* internal energy methods of cultivation such as those that this book introduces. Only if you cultivate your Qi can you achieve perfect mental clarity, optimum health and manifest your power to the maximum.

Thirty years from now you will certainly be a different person than you are now. The difference between ordinary people and the yogis or martial artists who excel is that they create in their minds an ideal of perfection, an idea of what they wish to become like and how they wish to change. Then they start working towards actualizing that ideal picture. They work towards that model, and then become like that. They create in their minds an ideal of their best self and then use the methods of self-cultivation, self-correction and self-perfection to gradually *become just like that* ... more of what *they want* in terms of the accomplishment of beingness. Why not aim for the highest?

You are living and aware due to possessing a mind and body, so that means you should develop them. The great gift of consciousness, the grand treasure within the most insentient universe, gives us the ability to always be transforming into something better. Therefore you should be working on perfecting our two attributes of mind and body.

Unfortunately, the martial arts and yoga are lacking in many of the teachings on internal energy that can take aspirants to the highest levels, but you will here be provided with the theoretical framework and training principles or routines that can guide you. If you build up a strong will to practice such techniques your *gong-fu* will rise towards the highest ideals you can envision.

3
FIXING THE FOUNDATION: RESTORING YOUR BODY TO MAXIMUM HEALTH

Jing transforms into Qi, Qi transforms into Shen, Shen transforms into Later Heavenly Qi, Later Heavenly Qi transforms into Primordial Spiritual energy. The yoga schools call all these energies the manifestations of Shakti, or primordial universal energy, which have evolved over time and compose different planes of being.

The human body is composed of Jing, and has internal vital energy called Prana or Qi. Thus, to become better at yoga and the martial arts we must start by focusing on our body made of Jing, and then later work on cultivating our Qi. We must first work to rejuvenate, replenish and repair our physical body, which is our genetic inheritance that came from our parents, in order to improve its health. Afterwards we can work on developing our internal energy, or Qi.

As cells age, the DNA/RNA replication process within them degrades. If through herbal detoxification efforts you can help your cells eliminate the cellular debris that accumulates inside them over time, or supply them with the nutrients that will help them perform their normal energy-hungry processes of detoxification, tissues will regenerate better. Consequently you will look younger, improve your health and live longer, which are the major goals of Taoism and yoga.

You should therefore take detoxification herbs on a regular yearly basis, and also supply your cells with extra COQ10 and other nutrients necessary for the heavy load of mitochondrial energy production required for the job of detoxifying cellular wastes. This is necessary because a lot of energy inside your cells is routed toward eliminating internal cellular wastes, and the extra energy you make available through nutrients will help to make this job far easier. Then your cells will have an excess of energy that they can devote to repairing themselves.

When taking such supplements, make sure you use superior supplement brands that work because supplements vary in quality and effectiveness across manufacturers even though they are labeled as "chemically identical."

Liver, sardines, oysters, spirulina, chlorella, mackerel, brewer's yeast and beans are also the best nucleotide-rich foods that will help repair cellular DNA/RNA or help build the RNA and DNA of new cells.

Green superfood and red superfood powders, which are extremely easy to digest and absorb because they are composed of micronized particles, can also supply vital nutrients in the most usable form for cellular growth and repair. These powdered juices, since they are composed of easily digested (highly absorbable) particles of high-density nutrition that you can mix with rice milk, almond milk, etc. or fresh juices, will supply your cells with a wide variety of different nutrients necessary for cellular detoxification, growth and repair. As particles, they constitute the most digestible and absorbable form of nutrients.

Shilajit, kelp powder, and colloidal minerals (only the Purest Colloids brand) can supply the most absorbable form of minerals possible. Most people nowadays are found to be mineral-deficient due to the poor quality of our soils, and they are also found to be nutritionally deficient in vitamins as well.[3] This necessitates vitamin and mineral supplementation in our diet, which will be a plus for your health.

---

[3] Worldwide, the most common nutrient deficiencies include iron, vitamin B6, vitamin D, folate, iodine and zinc. Vitamins A, C, E, calcium and magnesium are also under-consumed in most diets.

Also remember that people usually get fat whenever their diet contains too many simple sugars and carbohydrates, as well as vegetable oils. If you want to lose weight then cut down on your carbohydrate intake of grains and simple sugars, and also reduce your consumption of vegetable oils. Vegetable oils and sugar will definitely make you fat and weaken cellular membranes as well.

For health and longevity, your body's processes of assimilation and elimination must work well. They are dependent upon your circulatory system nourishing and cleansing your body through the blood supply. To open up your the capillaries and improve your blood circulation, pranayama practices are recommended but are not the only technique available. Special supplements and herbs can strip your arteries and capillaries free of cholesterol blockages and other occlusions to make them wider and more flexible, thus improving your blood circulation.[4]

A niacin flush will temporarily improve capillary blood circulation and raw tienchi powder will help to increase circulation as well. *Arnica Montana* and martial arts liniments can help heal muscle bruises. However, more permanent solutions for better blood circulation are warranted for yogis and martial artists.

The natural supplement nattokinase can dissolve blood clots within your blood vessels, and even open up the small capillaries leading to the retina and penis that may become occluded due to smoking, diabetes and other obstructive causes. Intravenous, rectal or oral EDTA can reduce calcified plaques within your arteries so as to increase the inner diameter of blood vessels and increase arterial flexibility. Even a small change in these factors will produce a huge improvement in your blood flow.[5] "Natures Pure Body Program" and other herbal combination formulas will detox the body by helping cells to rid themselves of accumulated wastes. Taking CoQ10 at the same time will give cells the extra energy necessary to help remove more cellular debris and thereby free up their energy for RNA/DNA repair and rejuvenation. Vitalzym and other enzyme supplement formulas can destroy

---

[4] See *Prevent and Reverse Atherosclerosis: Proven Natural Alternatives that Eliminate Cholesterol Plaque Without Surgery* by Stanton Reed.
[5] See *Detox Cleanse Your Body Quickly and Completely* by William Bodri.

circulating toxins in the blood.

Green superfoods and red superfoods (or juicing fresh vegetables) will supply cellular nutrition to the body in the most absorbable form possible, thus greatly helping with cellular DNA repair. Colloidal minerals, kelp powder and Shilajit will supply you with the minerals necessary for your body that are usually deficient in your diet. Shaking all the body's tissues by exercising on a Pogo stick, rebounder or standing on a Power Plate will exercise every cell in your body. Cells everywhere in the body will interpret the shaking as exercise and you will thereby derive the benefits of exercise without doing any work. Together with *actual* stretching exercises, this will enable the nutrient-rich fluids of the body to supply all cells equally via hydrodynamic waves that nourish every cell.

This total package of activities (nattokinase, cholesterol strippers, Vitalzym, Nature's Pure Body, COQ10, superfood powders, absorbable minerals, shaking exercises) thus becomes a way to dramatically cleanse your cells and circulatory system, which is also a channel of elimination. It will bathe each cell with nutrient-rich fluids that will improve cellular repair and rejuvenation. This protocol will exercise every body cell and tissue, encourage your cells to dump their internal debris into the bloodstream, and eliminate those poisons and other toxins within the bloodstream.

To help in this large task, solving constipation issues and keeping your liver and kidney healthy through yearly detoxification efforts is critical. Yearly detoxification efforts should include fixing any spinal vertebrae misalignments and attending to any physical repairs necessary to heal body damage or dysfunction. You must not just keep your circulatory system clean, but must keep your channels of elimination open, your physical structure in shape, your organs of detoxification healthy and in general your body healthy. This requires exercise and a clean diet.

For your sensory organs there are several commonly known remedies for improving the abilities of your senses: Zinc supplements usually restore the sense of taste and smell; Lion's Mane mushroom or Bacopa extracts *(bacopa monnieri)* can help restore the hearing; lutein, zeaxanthin, vitamin A, beta carotene, and the Bates method (or eyeglasses) can help restore eyesight;

DHA, good oils and non-oxidized micronized lecithin (derived from organic micro-milled non-GMO soybeans) can supply the purest nutrients to help build a great brain since it is mostly composed of fat. Basically, you should use whatever works to restore your sensory apparatus and to heal all the tissues of your body.

Blood Chemistry and CBC Analysis, by Dick Weatherby and Scott Ferguson, provides optimal reference ranges for blood markers that can help people identify the causes of medical conditions, and often suggests vitamin-mineral and herbal protocols for healing. Every home should have this book and reference it when you receive blood chemistry reports from your doctor or a hospital. It can help you catch things your doctor missed.

To restore one's vitality, sexual restraint and meditation are key. It is tradition but unsubstantiated that lamb bone marrow, sesame seeds, pistachio nuts and several other special foods can help restore male virility although meditation practice does indeed help with this task.

Chiropractic adjustments should be used to reset any bones out of place so that you optimize the structural alignment of your body's skeleton; a chiropractic "toggle adjustment" will realign your Atlas and Axis vertebrae (C1 and C2) alignment and thereby dramatically improve nervous system function (and thus athletic abilities) since the brainstem runs through these two vertebrae; Buhler's Advanced Muscle Integration Technique (AMIT) can be used to reactivate muscles that have been "shut off" due to accidental damage and which have therefore shifted some of their weight-bearing functions to adjacent tissues; Rolfing, Hellerwork, Swedish massage, active-release technique (ART), the Graston technique and many other bodywork methods can help fix muscular problems;[6] yoga (and Pilates or Activated Isolated Stretching, etc.) are excellent as passive athletic stretching exercises; active exercises such as martial arts, dance, sports and Ginastica Natural can be used to train your movements and mind-body coordination; pranayama practice will expand your lung volume, exercise your breath and improve inner Qi movements; *nei-gong* internal energy exercises will help you gain power, strength and entry into the spiritual sphere if done at a profound level … this list is far from complete, but

---

[6] *The 4-Hour Body* by Timothy Ferriss.

contains some of the many physical techniques you can rely upon to help nourish, heal and repair your body. The foundational task for yoga and the martial arts is to repair and rejuvenate your physical body made of Jing. Afterwards you can work at cultivating your energy or Qi.

Some specific miracle techniques are as follows: glucosamine sulfate and collagen peptides (Collagen 2 or Collagen 1&3) will help repair the cartilage in worn joints and heal (or prevent) knee problems; stem cell treatments can help repair a torn meniscus; HCG (human chorionic gonadotropin that is used to help people lose weight) and colloidal platinum (Purest Colloids) can regenerate (severed) nerve tissue; gin-soaked raisins will reduce arthritis pain and nodules in the fingers; vitamin B6 can sometimes cure tendonitis and carpal tunnel syndrome; nattokinase and EDTA chelation will dissolve blood clots and arterial occlusions; NeuroCranial Restucturing (bilateral nasal therapy) can open blocked sinus passages and eliminate recurrent migraine headaches; *Nauli Kriya* and plank hold exercises will help to prevent hernias that are common in men; leg splits, yoga exercises and *Mula bandha* will help open the pelvic muscles; using an Elgin Archxerciser will create flexibility for the bottom of the foot; an Ultraflexx foot rocker can be used to stretch your Achilles tendons, and Buhler's Advanced Muscle Integration Technique (AMIT) can reset inhibited Quadriceps, glutes and lower back muscles to help fix sprained or torn Achilles tendons damage permanently; acupuncture and deep tissue massage can help restore damaged muscles; Z-Health exercises that press on vital spots in the foot can stretch and strengthen the foot muscles and tendons; Terry Laughlin's Total Immersion method of swimming instruction can teach you to move through water more efficiently … these are some of the physical techniques you might use. Countless others are available.

From joints we move to tendons, from tendons to muscles, from muscles to internal energy. Z-Health exercises will lubricate all the joints of your body (especially opening the feet, spine, shoulders) by moving them in gentle circles; *Yi Jin Jing* stretches will easily strengthen the body's tendons and ligaments; yoga or Pilates will stretch all your muscles (make sure when stretching you always visualize the muscles under strain to send them Qi); martial arts or dance and athletics can used to master physical movements. *Qi-gong* and then *neijia* will enable you to control the Qi within your body.

To improve the body's posture, many modalities are available. There is the Feldenkrais method, Alexander technique, Natural Movement, Aston-Patterning, Dr. Eric Goodman's Foundation Training, Ginastica Natural (Natural Gymnastics) and the Yat Malmgren training for communicating emotions through movement that Sean Connery used when training to become James Bond. These are all wonderful techniques after you first correct any body misalignments.

First adjust your skeletal structure to its optimum by putting bones back into their proper positions, which means attending to their proper structural alignment within the skeleton, and afterwards you can use bodywork on your tendons, muscles and connective tissues such as NMT, myofascial release, strain-counterstrain, Barne's method, St. John's work, Rolfing, Egoscue, applied kinesiology, and so forth. Skeletal re-alignment and then muscular work should usually precede acupuncture in order to fix any underlying structural issues. There are lots of different bodywork therapies available.

These remedial methods for the body's repair and rejuvenation are important because we often damage our bodies through martial arts practice or just regular life. Through evolution the body has developed a structure that protects vital tissues via a hierarchy of priority that will sacrifice certain structures in order to protect others, and bodywork can be used to repair the most outer levels of protective damage.

For instance, your body will tighten muscles and make them immobile so that you avoid ripping an artery. It is also designed to sacrifice bones or even joints to protect arteries because if they tear you will die. The body's structure is designed to sacrifice muscles to protect joints, joints to protect lymphatics, lymph vessels to protect viscera (organs), organs to protect nerves, nerves to protect veins, veins to protect bones, and bones to protect arteries. This is a sequence to remember. Damage to knee joints, the Achilles tendon, hernias, and back problems are common human dysfunctions that are products of evolution and lifestyle so take special measure to protect these areas of the body in your training.

By stretching your body's muscles, tendons, ligaments and fascia you can develop them and re-orient their structure to greater capabilities. You can also learn how to align your body according to natural inner energy circulations that can be guided by your will, and which will thereby open up the Qi meridians within your body's tissues. *Nei-gong* practice is a way to do this as well as to transport and apply your internal Qi to heal your body, which is another reason to practice the internal martial arts.

Finally *qi-gong* and *nei-gong* practice, together with mental rehearsals and visualization efforts, will help you fully internalize mastery and reach a stage where you can unify your mind, body and Qi to create the unity we desire. The breathing exercises and inner energy work of these techniques will move your Qi throughout your muscular pathways and thus open up your body's Qi channels (*nadis*). Visualization together with your willpower (intent) can lead your Qi energy to body areas of your selection. When the Qi flows to a region due to these efforts, this can help remove various disorders in the location you are concentrating upon, and help heal it.

Remember that Qi/Prana flooding a region will tend to warm it and soften it. Mantras and emotion-provoking activities can excite your Qi to assume a certain characteristic nature that you wish, and you can use this fact in your Qi purification and channel opening practices. Such practices are necessary for the highest levels of yoga and the martial arts.

4
THE IMPORTANCE OF DAILY PRACTICE

As regards the physical practice of forms, or *wai-gong*, you need to practice the correct physical movements and basic body (external) alignments dependent upon your tradition. The standard forms for yoga *asanas* are also well-known. Since the correct mechanics of your particular practice need to be taught by your teacher, therefore nothing need be said.

However, it must be stated that if you want the *nei-gong* results of being able to manipulate your Qi, it is essential that you take inner Qi practice seriously. Most martial artists focus simply on muscle work but Qi work is the way to augment their performance. The internal and external of muscles and Qi must come together so that you can eventually use them as one.

The efficacy of your practice will depend not just on the amount of time you have practiced, but will mostly be determined by the quality of your practice. You will have to practice both breath work and internal energy movements led by your mind. In other words, *qi-gong* and pranayama that train your breathing will absolutely be necessary for reaching the highest levels of fighting ability. You will need to learn how to coordinate your breathing and internal energy with your movements.

In short, the highest levels of martial arts require knowledge and practice of spiritual methods. Collectively, such training will culminate in the germination of greater internal power derived from a harmonious blending of mind, body and spirit.

Internal energy, Qi, is the root and foundation of health and physical strength so a yogi or martial artist should work at building up this internal root. The internal arts of *nei-gong* stress optimal Qi circulation, natural movement, intention and a calm but alert mind. The external arts, *wai-gong*, focus on developing muscular strength, speed, flexibility, agility, endurance and athletic prowess. They teach how to exert force correctly in a variety of different ways where body parts are properly aligned so that power can be easily transmitted.

You first train the physical body, and then must train your Qi to become abundant and full. Then it can energize your physical body to a higher level so that your power can be manifested more effectively. This is one of the many reasons to practice inner energy work. Even yogis need these abilities. After developing your Qi, you need to match its movements with your physical movements and intent.

In order that you do not repeat errors when learning the physical movements, always try to practice correctly by maintaining the proper postures and alignments, even if this means you must work slower than you would like. Initially, martial arts training always teaches movements slowly so that you learn how to control your body when you are relaxed. Only after mastering a skill do you move on to the next stage of practice. If your practice repeats errors all the time, they will become deeply ingrained incorrect habits that will become difficult to break once you finally understand how to practice correctly. So practice slowly but correctly.

You must practice with perseverance and patience, which requires a strong will, dedication and a great deal of self-discipline. Practice without ceasing, the way is through self-practice. Once you make an activity repeatable, you will have made progress.

The mind trains the forms, the mind and forms train your Qi. Practice the internal and external separately, and later then combine so that you can use them as one. Practice matching the movement of your internal Qi with the movements of your external form so that the two align continuously without interruption. The outside and the inside should not be separated because from posture to posture the internal power should remain unbroken.

Wai-gong conditions your muscles, tendons, ligaments, joints, bones, posture and structure. It builds up the strength of your physical body, while *nei-gong* transforms your Qi and spirit. You train muscles externally, and train Qi internally. It takes years of effort to discover your real Qi, which can be as difficult as catching Hanuman's tail, and then many more years to learn how to use it.

You must learn how to open up restrictions to the Qi flow within your body. You must learn how to amass Qi inside yourself. You must learn how to circulate that Qi and direct it to different areas of your body. You must also "purify" your Qi and Qi circulatory channels through this training process. The ultimate goal is to learn how to coordinate your Qi circulation with external forms and your intent. When your mind and movements can lead your Qi efficiently, they will energize your muscles so that they can manifest your power to its maximum level. The goal is to fluently express Qi through your martial arts, and to be able to change its nature completely in an instant of thought. The goal is to flow with grace and ease in all your ordinary movements as well.

If you can get to the point where your Qi circulates everywhere without obstruction you will move with superior ease and grace and even be able to forget the feeling of your body due to optimal Qi flow. Achieving a fluent internal Qi flow means that your mind will become crystal clear and peaceful as well. Then you can experience both bliss and flow.

Some of these lessons or tips cannot be understood by beginners but only by advanced practitioners. Diligence in proper training is what ultimately determines your level of expertise. The harder you work and the more you refine your training the more you will advance. Once you see the benefits you will not stop. So become inspired. Don't let your potential go to waste.

The best advice as to the importance of practice is an old Chinese adage, *wo ming zai wo*, which means, "Every man forges his own destiny."

5
PROGRESSIVE PRACTICE: YOGA PRANAYAMA AND TAOIST *QI-GONG*

From Jing to Qi to Shen and then higher … from *wai-gong* to *qi-gong* to *nei-gong* to *Tao-gong*. These are the standard sequences of yoga and martial arts progression.

Cultivating your muscles and diet is focusing on your Jing. Cultivating your breathing and internal energy is focusing on your Qi. With the help of the sages and divinities of Heaven, cultivating your deepest vital energy and mental power is working on Shen. Progressing beyond the Shen stage of *nei-gong* to enter into real *Tao-gong*, you can then start working on much higher energies.

Always remember the first standard sequence of martial arts practice and progression: from *wai-gong* to *qi-gong* to *nei-gong* to *Tao-gong*. Always remember the second standard sequence of martial arts practice and progression: you start by working on your physical body composed of Jing, you next work on cultivating your vital energy Qi, you then progress to working on your spiritual energy Shen, you then start working on the Later Heavenly energy within your body, and finally you begin working on the Primordial Heavenly energy within your physical structure.

These are the practice roads for both gods and men.

Learning the correct diet, physical alignments and physical movements is cultivating your Jing. For Jing cultivation, your teacher will teach you the basic body mechanics of your form. If you learn an incorrect posture it will impede the flow of your Qi; an incorrect placement will lessen considerably the issuance of force and power during muscular expression.

For instance, the feet form the root of issuing *fa jin* explosive power from the body, therefore their placement, and that of the legs and waist, are crucial for being able to exert maximum power. The power of a punch comes from the big muscles of the lower body, and when the waist, torso, legs, arms and fists are properly aligned and coordinated they become incredibly efficient at delivering all that power. You need to learn their correct placements in any martial arts you practice.

In the soft martial arts of *tajiquan, baguazhang and xingyiquan,* the postures should reflect the most natural path for Qi circulation to flow as this allows for power to be transmitted full force. The postures should flow smoothly into one another where you cannot tell the end of one and beginning of another. The same principle is found in *vinyasa* yoga where there is a smooth transition from one *asana* (yoga posture) to another while the movements are paired with the breathing.

Each posture of a martial arts form is the external manifestation of leading Qi within your body from one part to another, and in an ideal situation your Qi should proceed seamlessly and without internal friction. Therefore the postures of the forms must be practiced absolutely correctly.

Qi work starts by mastering proper breathing, and then using it to cultivate your inner vital energy. Breath work, and then internal energy work, are the keys to improving both martial arts and yoga performance. Correct breathing will make a strong technique even stronger, and access to Qi energy will give it even more power and strength.

Correct breathing and better Qi flow can enhance your *root to the ground* and add impetus to your technique. Correct breathing and smoother Qi flow within your body can calm your mind and spirit. Correct breathing and proper Qi flow can increase the speed of your martial arts techniques and movements. For the highest martial arts, you must work on mastering correct breathing and improving the circulation of Qi within you so that it flows uninterruptedly, unbroken, in a smooth continuous fashion.

Thus, we first start the quest for higher internal energy by working on our breathing and then progress to developing inner Qi energy. We first work on *qi-gong* or respiration that affects superficial Qi, and then *nei-gong*.

Your breathing is used to ignite your "wind Qi" that is superficial in nature, and then after sufficient practice various exercises can finally touch upon your real Qi. This will then make you a true internal energy master. Once you work breathing and Qi into your martial arts you will start to improve significantly. Once you work Shen into it you will be at the highest levels of worldly training that leads to the doors of the Immortals.

Your "wind Qi" is also called "semblance Qi" or "semblance dharma" because it resembles the real, true, deep vital energy of your body that composes its underlying matrix. This real Qi of yours is difficult to activate, cultivate and transform. Breathing practices enable you to begin to recognize the superficial Qi of your body, which can then be used over time to finally activate your deeper, truest vital Qi energy.

Therefore, pay attention to the inner work you must do to cultivate Qi, for this separates the ordinary people from those who achieve truly transcendental attainments.

To cultivate your Qi, the automatic and deliberate processes of breathing must be regulated. First, start by practicing alternate nostril breathing to produce internal balance and harmony. Then practice holding your Qi at specific places within your body, and afterwards start circulating it within those regions to wash the tissues and free them of Qi flow restrictions. Practice performing hundreds to thousands of Qi rotations within your limbs and organs, and wash every area of the body over and over again including your fingers, toes, genitalia, nose and nasal cavity, teeth and gums, eyes and ears. Lead your Qi from one area to another. As your Qi begins to transform, learn to match it with your movements.

The *Yoga Sutras of Patanjali* teaches how to concentrate single-mindedly on points located inside your body, and the purpose of such concentration exercises is to lead Qi to those regions in order to "wash" or "purify" the tissues, which is called purification. If the tissues are washed long enough over the years, the energy matrix within them will become totally transformed by becoming free of impediments to Qi flow. It will become purified and strengthened. The pathways by which Qi travels within tissues will become free of obstructions, and your athletic excellence will improve.

You must also learn how to guide your Qi with countless revolutions along internal pathways, orbits, and circuits that correspond to the body's physical structure, including acupuncture meridians that are fascial planes of least resistance within the body.

Later you will be able to attain the skill of moving Qi throughout your entire body. This includes within all your muscles as well as throughout the marrow of your bones and your tendons, which are the soft extensions of the bone and harder to transform than muscles. The process of bone and tendon transformation is detailed within *The Tendon Metamorphosis Classic*, which is usually translated as *The Muscle and Tendon Change Classic (Yi Jin Jing)*. It contains classic methods for transforming the muscles and tendons. The secret to its techniques has just been explained.

You must eventually activate the deep real Qi within your limbs, torso, organs, muscles, tendons and bones – all your cells and tissues – and learn to match this vital energy with your movements.

Eventually after transforming the Qi matrix within all your tissues you want to attain a wholeness that links the Qi in each separate part of your body so that it becomes a single unified force and spirit. The energy of all parts must become connected as one whole and under the control of your mind. Then you can transform each martial arts posture and movement – which have the characteristics of shape, function and power – into their highest level of achievement.

The entire process starts by working to transform your Qi in various body parts, sections or along specific pathways of your body, and then learning how to use the transformed Qi with your muscular expression. An example is learning how to express muscular Qi power in your limbs by connecting (or routing) your muscular Qi with the Qi within your *dantian*. You must attain the ability for your Qi to move in an uninterrupted fashion from your lower *dantian* to the limbs for striking. Eventually you must achieve the principle within the *Taiji Classic* that the lower body must also become joined with your movements and Qi: "From the feet to the legs to the waist must be integrated, and become one unified Qi." This unification of Qi must be accomplished for the entire body.

The Qi within your body naturally moves in harmony with your pulse, breathing, blood pressure and posture. Just as with your blood, its circulation is affected by your body's structure and alignment. It takes years to learn the correct placement and alignment of your torsos and limbs so that Qi and power can flow through your body most efficiently. Maximum speed and power requires a precise alignment. If anything is off, such as errors in your posture or movements, then your Qi will move improperly because it will be impacted by obstruction, friction, or stagnation. In such situations you will feel the friction and then be unable to forget the sensation of your body (and thus identification with your body). You can only forget being a body or having a body if your body becomes healthy and its Qi flow becomes optimal.

A principle of practice is that your Qi follows your mind. In other words, your mind moves your Qi. This is because your Qi and consciousness are linked. Your thoughts can move your Qi, and internal Qi movements can give rise to thoughts. You can also use your breathing to affect your Qi just as your respiration surely affects the state of your mind. Secrets lie within these relationships that you can only discover through training.

The stage of *qi-gong* training entails a beginner's attempt to learn to guide the free energy in his body with his mind, which means training your will to move your Qi. Spinning it along circular pathways, coating organs and limbs, running up and down the spine, guiding it through all sorts of extensions, there are endless ways to move your Qi in order to wash all the structures and pathways of your body. Every time you do so, you should practice hundreds to thousands of repetitions.

After extensive intensified practices on your part that prepare your body for the transition, you will start to activate the true inner vital energy of your body that is deeper than the superficial wind Qi you can access through pranayama and *qi-gong* practices. Then you will start touching upon the stage of transcendental transformations that involve "real Qi" *nei-gong*. This is the stage of accomplishment responsible for the miraculous abilities of martial artists and yogis. There is a lot more to your body than just mechanical movements, and the secrets of your internal energy will remain a mystery until you enter the realm of *nei-gong*.

At first you will affect the superficial Qi of your body that guards your skin by forming a shield to protect you from negative outside influences such as the cold. Next, you can progress to touching a more interior Qi of your muscles and viscera that is more or substantial because it manages functions within your body. Finally you can attain to the level of Qi that penetrates your bones and absolutely all your tissues.

Because there are three levels of Qi that you must master – the superficial Qi of the skin, the Qi of the muscles and the Qi of the bones (bone marrow) – this is why Bodhidharma said of his best three students, "You have acquired my skin, you have acquired my meat, and you have acquired my bones." This did not just refer to varying comprehension of his dharma but levels of inner *gong-fu* attainment.

Everyone confusedly mistakes "wind *qi-gong*" for "real *nei-gong*," which involves a twelve-year period of transformation that purifies the Qi of your entire inner nature. Moving the superficial Qi within you, which feels like wind or a stream of water flowing within you, is easy to master through pranayama and *qi-gong* exercises. However, that success in easily generating internal sensations confuses students about the true level of their attainment. They usually think they have achieved the stage of real *nei-gong*, which takes years to reach, when they are just at the beginning stages of playing with superficial Qi. One progresses from moving the superficial free energy in your body (wind Qi) to ignite the body's real vital energy, and then the process is put under the supervision of Heaven.

In order to attain true internal power and strength, which only arises when you tap into this real Qi, you must first train your breathing and then progress onto moving your superficial vital energy with your mind, eventually matching it with your movements. Only after countless years of such preparatory work can you even approach touching your deepest vital energy. The real secret of martial arts is on the inside – this deep vital energy or real Qi.

Always remember the sequence, lest you become confused. The means of Qi practice progresses from muscular and respiratory *wai-gong* (where ordinary external breathing is practiced to become balanced, harmonious and uniform) to *qi-gong* (through pranayama and breath work you learn to control the movement of superficial Qi within your body and along meridians until you can put mind, body and breath into a union of practice) to *nei-gong* (where your true internal energy is activated and starts automatically moving from place to place to wash you internally) to *Tao-gong* (the highest level of martial arts equivalent to a divine status).

Here are the methods, therefore, of training your Qi:

(1) You can mentally focus attention on a region of your body for a prolonged period of time to pull your body's Qi into that area and thereby concentrate the Qi within that region. This happens when you visualize "chakras" inside certain body areas, or simply concentrate on feeling the shape of your limbs. Such concentration pulls Qi to those regions of sustained focus. You can also concentrate on feeling the entirety of an appendage or extremity, meaning that you try to feel all the "meat" within the shape of a body region. Maintaining stable concentration on an area of your body – without necessarily stretching or moving it in any special way - will pull your Qi into that area, and that concentration of Qi is a type of activation that will "wash" or purify the region's underlying energy matrix that is composed of Qi. This energy matrix passes through all body tissues like a network of atomic bonds. In yoga, concentrating upon and holding the Qi at certain body locations is always used for this purpose of washing your inner subtle energy structure, and is called "opening the *nadis*" whereas in Chinese martial arts this is called "opening your Qi channels." You put your awareness on an internal location within your body, your Qi is then

pulled into that location because of your concentration, and then the concentration of Qi warms and softens the obstructions in Qi flow within it, and then moving Qi pushes through those knots and obstructions. In Chinese martial arts this opening or purification work is done through a variety of methods. This method of holding your focused concentration on body parts while you hold a stationary position (or are moving naturally) draws your Qi into those regions. Next, you can try to stimulate the area's Qi by using various add-ons such as reciting mantra sounds from within the location, arousing certain emotions on a large scale to affect the entire Qi of your body while so doing, or imagining a shining light within that region or some other change to the sensations within that region. It is common to imagine a bright flame, fiery hotness, shining sun, trickling water, cooling moon or other symbol of Yang Qi or Yin Qi inside a region whose Qi channels you wish to open and whose Qi you wish to purify. You basically concentrate to excite the local Qi within a region. These methods will tend to stimulate, energize, or invigorate the Yin Qi or Yang Qi of an area, thus vibrating its underlying network of Yin and Yang essence for the purposes of purifying the area's Qi of defilements that impede Qi flow within it.

(2) In yoga you are taught to hold a static, unmoving *asana* that tenses muscles while maintaining mental emptiness (the formless mental state of not thinking). In the Chinese martial arts, people undertake *Zhanzhuang Gong* training (Standing Stump Development) by holding a stationary standing posture that may or may not strain muscles while their mind remains empty and still. Some yoga *asanas* or stationary standing forms in the martial arts, by design, are used to assist and guide the circulation of Qi throughout the meridians of your body. In *Zhanzhuang Gong* practices you are instructed not to play with your thoughts or let them wander but to cultivate mental stillness or "empty mind" while you stand in the form. This mental quiescence allows Heaven to come to your aid to help you open your Qi meridians and transform your muscle Qi. This assistance only becomes possible when you cultivate a quiet mind since thoughts then don't interfere with Heaven's involvement in helping your Qi flow get better. Sometimes mantras are therefore recited to request heavenly aid during martial arts standing practices. When your body is holding stationary yoga *asanas* that stretch muscles, or stable martial arts positions such as the Trinity Posture (*San Ti Shi*) of *xingyiquan,* the Eight Mother Palms holding

postures of *baguazhang*, or various *Shuzuang Bu* (Tree Stump) postures and other practices, you can alternately practice pushing or pulling your Qi through the muscles being stretched. You can also apply visualization efforts on the muscles being exercised by "grabbing their Qi" and trying to energize it in various ways such as by imagining that the muscles change color, start glowing with bright light, feel heavier or lighter or denser and so on. You can also hold your breath with *kumbhaka* pranayama practices while visualizing that your Qi accumulates within you and starts opening up your area of focus. You can also mentally focus on just feeling the shape of the muscles, which is also a method of activating the Qi in the muscles. As stated, during stationary postures you can also use mental efforts to make your muscles and limbs feel lighter (*laghima siddha* or *ching gong*) or heavier (*garima siddhi*), which is done by trying to absorb lofty, agile, light Yang Qi or heavy, rooted Yin essence while holding a posture or *asana*. You can recite mantras or seed syllables (*bijas*) as if originating from within those muscles in order to shake their Qi and purify them of circulatory obstructions. For this method, the best mantas or sounds to use are those that strongly vibrate the muscles or seem to resonate strongly within the focus area because those sounds stimulate the Qi within the region of interest. Masters can suggest the best sound, *bija* or mantra for each body location or you can experiment on your own. Whilst using this type of sound yoga on body parts, which is called Mantrayana, you can also try to vitalize or exhilarate your entire body with strong Yin Qi or Yang Qi emotions because this will help to add additional movement to your Qi, which is a practice method within Nyasa Yoga. This will serve to further purify the Yin or Yang Qi within the matrix of your muscles and rid them of "knots" or obstructions that impede smooth and efficient Qi flow. Wherever you put your concentration within your body your Qi will automatically follow because Qi and consciousness are linked. *Emotions produce sensations within all the cells of your body.* Those sensations are vibrational energy, and affect your Qi with a certain frequency that we might call a "tone." Hence, if you add feelings and emotional content to your practice session by arousing certain emotions that are either Yin or Yang in nature, you will thereby wash all your tissues with those Yin or Yang energies. This will greatly enhance your efforts to cultivate *both Yin and Yang Qi within your body*, which is necessary for the highest attainments. In some martial arts, masters often use stationary standing practices to draw energy into their bodies through a point on the top of their head (or through all its pores) or in their feet, and sometimes practice at special Yin or Yang periods of the day to pull in different energies. The purpose is to feed the body Yin or Yang energy during a stationary posture, amass Qi in the body's interior, and then feed it to the limbs or to the entire network of Qi channels (*nadis*) within the body. You typically practice inhaling energy into your *dantian* where it will then disperse to all other regions of the body.

(3) You can try to maintain a painful martial arts form such as the horse stance, or a yoga posture that is initially painful such as the sitting lotus meditation position, whose difficulty of muscular strain forces your Qi to push through the muscles in order to maintain its normal circulation. Typically you are to cultivate mental peace and emptiness during such practices where there is not a ripple of thought. For some schools, however, you try to guide your Qi through the straining muscles while you maintain an uncomfortable posture without collapsing. However, usually you want to remain mentally empty and relaxed while your muscles and Qi do all the circulatory work without any pushing efforts led by your will. In the martial arts, proficiency in holding standing leg postures begins once the legs stop shaking since that proves that the muscles have been strengthened and the Qi pathways within them have somewhat opened. This usually requires many months of training where you hold postures without moving. To achieve the proficiency of steadiness in many positions – where the Qi is forced to push through tissues on its own – you must endure the fire of pain, trembling, shaking, perspiration, and the sensation of collapsing while maintaining them. Or, you can also use your own mechanical force to pump your Qi through specific body locations as in yoga exercises like *mula bandha*, and thereby wash hard-to-reach body cavities with Qi in this way. *Kumbhaka* pranayama, where holding your breath forces your lungs to expand and your capillaries to dilate, is another method used to forcibly push Qi through body regions to purify them.

(4) You can *wash* a body region or appendage with your Qi by mentally circulating it in various ways within that area – up, down, clockwise, counterclockwise, inside, outside, etcetera. Using mind power, you rotate your Qi in a selected spot, which is therefore called washing or cleansing. You mentally lead your Qi to a specific body area or part and then rotate it

in various ways over and over again within and around that area, and you must repeat such washings hundreds of times per session. *All parts of your body including the internal organs, the four limbs, and hundreds of bones must be completely washed and cleaned individually.* Or, you can use very special techniques to exercise or stretch an anatomical part in order to specifically help its Qi circulation, and then use some method to improve that circulation through encouragement. Some examples are rolling wooden balls in *taijiquan* and Lion Shape *baguazuang* in order to develop Qi in the fingertips by enlivening them with Qi; humming "mmm" when trying to feel and then push your Qi through the upper palate of your mouth; reciting the sounds "Cha" and "Chr" when trying to push or pull the Qi through your teeth and gums; pushing your tongue up against your palate to stretch its muscles *and* the muscles of the thyroid and throat (pushing against the roof of the mouth moves the muscles within your thyroid) while simultaneously reciting the sound of "Ham" or "Jha" in the thyroid since this will vibrate the Qi in that region. Touching the palate with the tip of your tongue curled backwards is a method used in martial arts and yoga that provides a bridge so that you can use your mind to circulate your Qi through your tongue to your upper palate, and then in various rotational patterns within the back of your throat, the nasal cavity, cerebellum, and so forth. The idea of concentrating on the spot between your forehead in meditation brings Qi to that region, but few people know the secret that you should also pull that Qi into your nasal cavity behind that spot and perform various revolutions to wash those structures. To transform your eyes, whose *bija* cultivation sound is "Ra," they should be relaxed while you imagine gently pulling light (Qi) into them and on through to the back of your head, where you can then wash your cerebellum and visual cortex with the Qi. For transforming the brainstem (known as the "muddy pellet" in Chinese Taoism and the *Ajna chakra* in yoga) and surrounding structure of the brain, you should revolve your Qi in circulations guided by diffusion tensor imaging (DTI) pictures of your brain's nerves, which are the petals of the *Sahasrara chakra*. The brain is actually the *Sahasrara chakra* of yoga whose petals are its countless neurons. All these methods involve swishing your Qi around a region to invigorate and cleanse it.

(5) Your Qi follows your mind in harmony with your breathing. You can guide your Qi through various circuits in your body, moving it from point

to point and location to location, to wash various regions in sequence. This will gradually free the circulatory flow of those pathways from obstructions. Afterwards you must link the Qi of these separate regions as one connected, unified whole. In yoga you lead Qi from place to place to create clear internal circulatory pathways, and also progressively wash your entire body in total with Qi. In the martial arts you try to feel the Qi of a specific muscular linkage or acupuncture pathway, and work on opening up the Qi routes within the pathway because this will make the associated muscular movements more efficient. The external movements of the body in martial arts, when coordinated with your breathing, can also assist the internal movement of Qi flow throughout your meridians. In the soft martial arts the muscles and tendons should remain relaxed as much as possible because practicing softness allows your Qi to move more freely along its muscular routes. When the body is soft your Qi circulation improves, so muscular stiffness is avoided in the soft martial arts as well as in *qi-gong* and *nei-gong* practices. Softness also allows your Qi to more easily move from your lower body regions and *dantian* to your limbs, which is beneficial for striking. The hard martial arts styles focus on strengthening the muscles, and rely on muscles tensing up with Qi in order to energize muscular power to maximum efficacy. In both cases, whether the muscles are soft or hard, practice involves leading your Qi to your muscles to energize them, which washes those pathways of blockages and defilements that might impede smoother circulatory flow. Therefore you must learn how to use your mind to lead your Qi efficiently. After many years of practice in accumulating Qi, storing Qi, and washing different body sections with Qi, by then repeatedly running Qi through circuitous routes you will make those Qi flows more efficient and muscular movements more powerful. Furthermore, by seamlessly linking internal sections of Qi together as a single unit, you can eventually fill all your limbs and torso with Qi so that you ultimately become a single body of energy, which is what you ultimately are. When you feel this attainment then you actually attain a certain stage of flow and start cultivating the practices of the sages and Immortals.

(6) Eventually after using all these techniques you will build to the point where you can feel the entire Qi of your body as a unified whole because the Qi of all individual parts becomes connected. You first cultivate the Qi of individual body regions or appendages, next thread them together in

pathways, and ultimately connect them as a single seamless whole. Various intensified yoga practices are available for bypassing this process of working on segments and pathways and feeling the entire Qi of your body as a single unit. In other words, exercise are available for cultivating that internal Qi wholeness directly without needing to concentrate on individual parts whose energies afterwards must be threaded together into a continuous whole. The point of all these techniques is to try to first encourage Qi movement through your muscles by stretching them, mentally focusing (concentrating) on them, or by guiding the Qi through them, and in this way "wash" them with Qi purification. Whether you are practicing martial arts or yoga, this is the basis of *anapana,* Vajrayana, *kriya yoga, kundalini yoga,* inner alchemy, internal martial arts, *nei-gong, neijiaquan, neijia,* etc. Eventually you can feel the entire Qi of your body as a single unit, and its internal circulation becomes everywhere orderly and free of impediments, obstructions or dysfunctions. Then you can experience a peaceful clear mind and an internal state of flow. At the highest level of attainment, you can tap into the deepest underlying energy matrix of your body that penetrates even through the bones, an accomplishment due to having cleansed all your tissues and internal pathways, and you can attain the state of "no extremities" or "no body" where you hardly notice your body anymore because your body has become healthy and the Qi flow is so excellent. When your Qi flows so smoothly and comfortably throughout your body, your mind will become empty, calm, clean and clear and you will become able to forget the physical sensations of having a body. Hence, your body and mind will become blissful within both movement and non-movement.

As you can see, there are moving and stationary forms of *qi-gong* and *nei-gong.* The training involves using your mind to guide/lead your Qi by willpower (intent), and then doing so in various patterns hundreds of times per practice session.

When practicing such techniques, always try to feel the Qi within the body location being emphasized rather than just imagine you are moving it. There is often a great disconnect between the Qi within your body that you are trying to move and the visualization efforts performed in your brain. Often you may think you are moving your Qi during a practice session, but you are not actually feeling any physical sensations in your body because your thought isn't connected with that area. In that case your thoughts or will (Yi) are not moving your Qi. You thoughts have to connect with the Qi that you are trying to move, and you must feel it at that location.

You could spend years in wasted effort if your mental thoughts do not connect with actual Qi circulations in your muscles and organs, which *is the important thing* because you want to learn how to move your Qi with your mind. Thinking about moving your Qi is different than actually doing it, which is the point of such practices, *so make sure that what you intend to do is felt within your body* because you are supposed to connect your will and intent with your Qi in the region of focus. This circulation of Qi will transform or purify the Qi in those regions.

Furthermore, your emotions will affect your inner Qi flow, which is why adding emotional toning to your practice can change the flavor of your Qi in terms of its Yin and Yang temperament.

The best type of practice involves a calm and peaceful mind since this supports the most natural Qi flow. Thus, meditation practice is encouraged for both yoga and the martial arts. Specifically, one should practice what is known as empty mind, formless mind, stillness, quiescence, tranquility or letting go of thoughts meditation that produces a peaceful mind of serenity and calmness.

The purpose of emptiness meditation is to let Qi arise within you while you maintain mental clarity and an openness that does not cling to those sensations, which would inhibit that Qi flow or push it in an unnatural direction. In a state of tranquility and quiescence, the natural potential of your life force develops and starts moving within your body, which can even heal illness as well as defer decline and aging. This is the force you develop through *nei-gong* and employ in the highest martial arts. You want to let it arise within you and refrain from interfering with its activity of running through your Qi channels and cleansing them of obstructions. Whenever you feel such sensations or warmth you are usually feeling the friction of Qi flow within the channels, but the friction will decline after those circulatory routes become free of impediments.

The ultimate objective of all these practices is to match your Qi with your martial arts and natural physical movements so they have more grace and ease and seem to flow into one another. In the martial arts, exercising the body in the right way, with the right alignment and movements, is most important for proper Qi flow. These are some of the pathways of preparatory work that build to a superior result.

6
BREATH TRAINING THROUGH *QI-GONG*
AND PRANAYAMA PRACTICES

Of all the cultivation methods that purify the body's Qi and Qi channels, detoxification[7] through pranayama and *qi-gong* are considered the best. The sage Vyasa said, "There is no greater austerity than pranayama to remove impurities." The *Hatha Yoga Pradipika* states, "Some teachers state that all impurities are removed by pranayama alone."

Like using an appliance to blow air to clean an object, pranayama uses breath to push out the impurities within your body. In particular, pranayama practice pushes clear any blockages within the Qi channels of your tissues. It is the most important of the eight limbs of yoga.

When your Qi channels have not been fully opened in all your tissues because of impurities, impediments and bottlenecks, your Qi flow is inhibited in some areas within your body. Body bliss is then unattainable, and the flow state remains out of reach. Therefore you should practice pranayama to open up all your inner energy pathways. This includes within your brain, which will calm consciousness, and within your muscles and organs to eliminate physical discomfort.

The purpose of pranayama methods is to wake up and open all the vital

---

[7] See *Detox Cleanse Your Body Quickly and Completely* by William Bodri.

energy channels in every section of your body. If the pathways are purified of obstructions through pranayama and breathing exercises then you can accumulate more, retain more and circulate more Qi within your body. You will see an increase in stamina, become able to strike with more force, move faster, and in general improve your athletic abilities. Your health, longevity and mental clarity will improve as well.

By the practice of pranayama, in connection with inner visualization work and mental concentration, you purify your body for *nei-gong* and the higher martial arts.

The standard pranayama exercises of yoga include *Bhastrika* "bellows breathing," *Visama Vritti* "uneven breathing," *Anuloma* "with the grain (natural)" pranayama, and *Kapalabhati* "skull shining" pranayama. These can be practiced as you deem fit. The initial stage of pranayama practice involves alternate breathing exercises to balance your breath and Qi, and then *kumbhaka* breath retention (holding) exercises to more forcibly push out the impurities within your Qi channels.

ALTERNATE NOSTRIL BREATHING

One simple pranayama method for harmonizing your breath is to sit down in a comfortable position and inhale through your left nostril deeply into your lungs *and the left side of your body*. Inhale so that you feel that the entire left side of your body fills with Qi from head to toes. After retaining the breath as long as possible you should exhale slowly through your right nostril. Next, repeat the same process using your right nostril for inhalation, feel your breath suffusing the entire right side of your body, and then use your left nostril for exhalation.

Always use as few muscles as possible to retain the breath within your body. Also, hold your breath to the utmost limit possible without straining any muscles until your body begins to tremble, or perspiration breaks out, and then exhale slowly. If a teacher instead advises you to exhale quickly then follow his instructions.

The general principle for breath retention practices is to hold your breath *as deeply within your body as possible, for as long as possible, using as little force and as few muscles as possible*, and then slowly expel it or forcibly expel it as quickly as possible according to instructions.

You can also perform this specific exercise in a different way by sending the energy up the left or right side of your spine, or holding it within the spine rather than filling the entire left or right side of your body. You also have the option of using both nostrils simultaneously for inhalation and exhalation instead of alternately. You inhale through both nostrils, retain the air within your body as deeply as possible and for as long as possible, and then exhale through both nostrils while guiding the energy up your spine. This will also help to balance the Qi within your body.

Alternate nostril breathing exercises help to harmonize your breathing patterns. When your breathing and Qi are harmonious, the body is naturally strong. But if you do not breathe in deep enough to feel the Qi in the entire left or right sections of your body, or cannot feel it in a designated section or region, or within your whole body as an entirety, then what good is it for balancing your Qi? Deficient in these measures, it is then just a superficial exercise without any real benefit.

The next progression in difficulty are the following exercises performed in a sitting position, or by sitting on the floor with both your legs stretched out in front of you. Draw the air through the left nostril into your lungs, filling your lungs deeply and fully, and hold your breath at two places: your left big toe and within your entire lower abdomen (and leg stretching to the toes) until you can retain it no more. Then expel it with force. Next, in the same manner, fill up the lungs deeply with air through the right nostril, hold it at the right big toe and within your lower abdomen beneath the navel (and leg), and then expel it quickly when it can no longer be retained. Always concentrate on feeling your breath within your lower belly, pelvic girdle (with genitalia), along the legs, and make sure the feeling of energy reaches the toes.

The next level of difficulty is to sit on the ground with legs outstretched in a triangular manner, inhale deeply awhile bending to one side, and grab your big toe. While holding your breath try to gently lead it along the leg, especially concentrating on the leg's inner side, until you can feel it in your ankles, bottom of the foot, and big toe. When you can retain it no longer then exhale. Repeat for the other leg. Do this several times consecutively.

As with the horse riding stance that martial artists practice holding to strengthen their muscles and open their leg meridians, this exercise will help to open up the Qi channels of your legs too.

KHUMBHAKA AND NINE-BOTTLED WIND PRACICE

Of all the pranayama methods, *kumbhaka* pranayama methods that entail holding the breath are the most important. Consistently practiced with discipline, they can increase your lung capacity by about 20-30%. After *kumbhaka* breath retention practices help you open up more Qi channels, then you can store more Qi within your body.

There are many different *kumbhaka* techniques. The *Gheranda Samhita* contains eight different *kumbhaka* pranayama techniques, called "pots," because you hold your breath in your lungs just as things are held within a pot. You may practice these as you wish.

A very powerful *kumbhaka* technique is the Nine-bottled wind, "Nine Segment Breathing" (*Jiujie Fofeng*) or "Nine winds" practice of Tibetan Buddhism attributed to the female Buddha Vajravarahi. Every day you must measure how long you can hold your breath with this superior technique, keeping a record so that you can gradually strive for a longer period of breath retention over time.

The principles to grasp for the practice are to hold your breath as deep within your body as possible, for as long as possible, using as little force with as few muscles as possible, and then to forcibly expel it as quickly as possible when you can no longer hold it inside. The method:

(1) Sit in an upright position.

(2) Visualize your body becoming as clear as crystal.

(3) Close your mouth and also close your left nostril completely by raising your left arm perpendicular to your torso, and press your left hand's index finger against the left nostril to shut it. Your right arm should be fully extended and pushing against your right leg calf in order to raise your chest and spread your ribs.

(4) Start slowly inhaling air deeply into your lungs through your right nostril. The inhalation should consist of a long breath that goes deep inside you and penetrates as deep into your abdomen as possible. During your inhalation, visually imagine that your body becomes filled with a shining bright light that eliminates any internal obstructions or impediments to Qi flow. Continue inhaling as slowly and deeply as possible until you are full and can inhale no longer.

(5) Now relax your body as much as possible while holding your breath trapped inside you. Hold your breath for as long as possible, but use as few muscles as possible to do so. Don't tighten any muscles so that your Qi can start opening up all the tiny energy pathways in your body without having to fight muscle tension.

(6) When you can hold your breath no longer, expel it as quickly and forcefully as possible through the open right nostril. Forcefully expel the air out of your body quickly to complete one cycle or round of this exercise.

(7) Repeat this exercise of slow inhalation, long retention, and forceful exhalation two more times for a total of three times for the right nostril. All the while your left nostril should be kept closed with your raised left arm and hand while the active nostril is the right nostril.

(8) Now switch hands so that the right arm is raised perpendicularly to your side and the right hand's index finger now pinches shut the right nostril while the left nostril remains open. Your left arm is locked in an extended position parallel to your torso and presses against your left calf in order to raise the chest and spread the ribs somewhat. Inhale through your left nostril following the same instructions as before, hold your breath for as long as possible and then forcefully exhale. Repeat this exercise three times

for this side of the body. Thus, six repetitions of this exercise will now have been completed.

(9) When the left and right nostril breathings are both done, extend both your arms down to push upon your calves, locking your elbows, and by so doing lift up your chest. Inhale slowly through both open nostrils, hold your breath within your lungs and abdomen as deeply as possible for as long as possible. Then exhale quickly by shooting the air out from your nostrils. Do this for a total of three times.

Altogether nine inhalations and breath retentions are performed using this simple technique of alternate nostril breath retention, which gives rise to the name of "Nine-step Bottled Wind" practice or "Nine winds" *kumbhaka* practice.

FREEDIVING BREATH TRAINING

To increase the amount of time you can hold your breath (breath retention), you can combine your *kumbhaka* practices with the training methods for underwater freediving. This will usually add one or more minutes to the amount of time you can retain your breath inside you, which is beneficial since it will help you clear out more Qi channels.

In freediving breath training, you first relax your body by putting it in a comfortable sitting or prone position. You then take a deep breath where you first fill your stomach and lower *dantian* with breath, and then the lower section of your lungs, and finally the upper sections of your lungs until completely full. The exhalation should last for double the amount of time it took you to breath in, so if you inhaled for four seconds you would exhale for eight seconds after filling with breath and retaining it.

You do this exercise for about three to four minutes before you want to take your final breath for going underwater. You take in the deepest breath you can, stomach filled first and thereafter the chest and upper lungs, and retain it for as long as possible until you surface.

During freediving dry land practice for holding your breath, you ignore your diaphragm when it starts contracting because the point is to train yourself to hold your breath for as long as possible. Contractions start because carbon dioxide builds up within your body rather than because your oxygen is depleted, so when you start experiencing contractions you still have lots of oxygen available and can retain your breath longer. At that point, being able to continue holding your breath comes down to mental training.

In pranayama practice it is the same in that you can learn to hold your breath far past the point where muscle contractions start, which is when the practice really starts to significantly force impediments free from your Qi channels. Yogis hold *asanas* for health and well-being, but they practice pranayama to eliminate sickness and lengthen their life span so they are interested in longer and longer retention times. As you get older, you need to do more pranayama because it will help your health and longevity.

The spiritual reasons for practicing pranayama is that it enables the body to hold more Qi and also improves the internal flow of your life energy. Martial artists need to understand that more Qi and better Qi flow will increase your internal power. In fact, the more *you become Qi yourself* or touch the utmost energy matrix of your body the higher will be your level of practice.

Because pranayama practice can open up the Qi channels (*nadis*) within the brain and cause better Qi flow into the head, pranayama exercises can sharpen the intellect, sharpen the senses, and help quiet a wandering mind. It helps with concentration. Pranayama develops the brain, the head, your lung capacity, the strength of your breathing and your longevity. Through the power of pranayama you can develop strength in your bones, bone marrow, and heart. All these are important factors necessary for health maintenance.

Breath retention pranayama practices should definitely be practiced along with yoga *asanas* and martial arts forms. When practicing you need to spend as little energy as possible holding your muscles of breath retention. You must diligently practice every day, measure your progress every week, and thereby gradually increase retention. Because *kumbhaka* practices can cause harm if you attempt too much too quickly, or try to use too much force, always progress gradually in breath retention exercises. Just as you should be soft when learning the internal martial arts, you should try to be as soft as possible when performing *kumbhaka* practices, and in this way you will make progress and avoid harm.

Practiced four times per day on an empty stomach, do not think *kumbhaka* practices worthless. In time your Qi will internally flow better everywhere, and you can much more easily connect your life force with your movements where your mind, Qi and limbs all become unified. The basis of mind-energy coordination is such work, and the basis of linking consciousness with your own vital energy is to move both in unison.

Ancient yoga traditions teach that we should practice pranayama after *asana* practice. However, Master Sun Lu-Tang, founder of Sun style *taijiquan*, taught that martial artists who train in *taijiquan, baguazhang* and *xingyiquan* should first practice a period of *qi-gong* before each training session and then practice the forms. He would himself practice several hours of *qi-gong* and then remain in a standing posture cultivating stillness, after which he would enter into physical practice. Yogis practice *asanas* first, and then pranayama.

OPENING THE CIRCULATIONS THROUGH BREATHING

Martial artists must gain proficiency in being able to hold their breath, breath in special ways (in tune with their movements), and guide their Qi inside their bodies. In the early stages of *qi-gong* practice the prime directive is to use your breathing (or your mind that can guide your Qi) to open up the microcosmic orbit that spans the front and back of your body like a circular orbit. You can use your breathing to move your Qi to open up this pathway, which is composed of two acupuncture meridians, or you can use your mind to lead your Qi along this channel.

The objective is to open up this major Qi pathway by ridding it of impediments. They are eliminated by continuous run-throughs of Qi, led by your breathing or mind, which are like using an ox to plough a field. The microcosmic orbit is a continuous circular Qi circulation along the *du mai* and *ren mai* meridians located in the spine and down the front of the body.

The *du mai*, or governing meridian, carries ascending Qi from your perineum up through your sacrum and spine across the top of your head to your nose and lips. The *ren mai*, or conception meridian, carries descending Qi down the front of the body from the lower lip to your perineum, which is located next to your anus at the very lowest spot on your torso. A neglected aspect of the downward Qi circulation within the body is the Qi flow through our mouth through the esophagus to the stomach, intestines and anus. Since this alimentary tube is the essence of our body that evolved from worms, it is critical that this passageway be cultivated through inner *nei-gong* exercises that run Qi along its length. Another neglected descending pathway is to pull your Qi downwards along the course of your endocrine glands starting from your brain and running to your genitals. This is a internal communication network that works by transmitting hormonal messages within the body rather than nerve impulses.

It is no secret that top martial artists, and yogis, regularly engage in stillness practices such as empty mind meditation (see Appendix for practice details). When the mind becomes too busy during your meditation practice you are often advised to use that energy by switching to breathing practices, such as pranayama, that will open up your Qi channels and wash your body's tissues with Qi. This will also tend to calm your mind. Meditation practice goes hand in hand with breath work and Qi work.

The Tientai school of Buddhism has many special breathing practices employed by martial artists, many of whom became enlightened by associating themselves with this school and employing its methods. In India much yoga pranayama work is done in the school of Mantrayana, which uses the rhythm of physical breathing as a coordinating mechanism for mantras, inner energy work and visualization practices. Taoism has many breathing techniques used by martial artists as well, all of which are designed to move your Qi and help open up the pathways of Qi circulation within your body.

Correct breathing technique is important to mastering *gong-fu*. Here are some popular Taoist breathing practices used by martial artists.

During sitting meditation practice Taoists are taught to spin their Qi through the microcosmic circuit – the loop connecting the conception and governing meridians (*ren mai* and *du mai*) – in order to open up these meridian pathways. They are taught to use their mind to revolve their Qi along this circuit hundreds of times per day. Variations of this basic technique are found in many traditions and including wiggling your Qi in various ways through each vertebrae of your spine, sucking Qi into each spinal vertebrae, concentrating on each separate spinal vertebrae, or leading Qi up and down the spine hundreds of times per practice session. Countless variations on sending Qi up and down your spinal column are used.

Now, you must understand that all of the systems of "highest yoga tantra" in Tibet, and many yoga practices within India, explain that you should visualize the body's left and right Qi channels within your spine, and then using breathing methods (or mental imagination) to redirect those energies into opening the *sushumna* central channel of the spine. Frankly, you just lead energy into the spine and then any and all Qi channels within it open because of the effort. Such practices usually involve taking a full deep breath in, holding that breath for around 15-20 seconds while you move the energy up the spine, and then letting it go.

There are two simple Taoist martial arts methods, to be used during sitting meditation practice, where you use your breathing to connect with your Qi energy in order to open these meridians.

The *first method* is as follows. Using just one breath, you inhale and use that energy to take your Qi from your tailbone (sacrum) up your spine and across the top of your head to the nose. Exhaling you take the internal energy from your nose down the center of the front of your body to your abdomen, then to your perineum and finally back to the sacrum. This is to open up your microcosmic (*du mai* and *ren mai*) circulation.

Another one-breath alternative is to inhale, and with that inhalation take your Qi from your nose down the front of your body and through the perineum to your tailbone. Exhaling you then lead your Qi from your sacrum up your spine, across your head and down your face to your lips.

At an advanced stage of microcosmic circulation practice, when you inhale and lead your Qi over the top of your head, you should simultaneously take the Qi *through your brain* because that's where the major Qi channels are located. When exhaling you should simultaneously lead the Qi *down the center of your body* through your esophagus, stomach and intestines to your perineum. This is a more advanced but more powerful technique than simply leading Qi down the front centerline of your body. It helps you open up the Qi channels within your brain and along your worm-like alimentary canal that is the center of your body and core of your physical nature. For instance, you can lead your Qi up your spine to your brain, circulate it through your brain, and then pull it down through the empty nasal cavities to the throat, stomach and then intestines (*dantian*). No one does this, but for those who do your *gong-fu* will accelerate appreciably. You can also lead the Qi downwards from the brain by following a descending pathway of glands as follows: brain, salivary glands in the mouth, thyroid gland in the throat, thymus gland in the chest, pancreas, adrenal glands atop the kidneys, prostate or ovaries, and then perineum.

A *second method* for opening up the microcosmic circulation, using two breaths instead of just one, is possible. With your first inhalation you lead the Qi from your nose to your lower abdomen (*dantian*). Exhaling that same breath, you lead the Qi from the lower abdomen to your tailbone. With the next inhalation, you lead your Qi from your tailbone up your spine to the level of the shoulders, and upon exhalation lead the Qi over your head to your nose to complete the cycle.

After an individual masters microcosmic breath circulation, they can go on to learn the "five breaths" method for opening the Qi circulatory route of the *macrocosmic orbit* (*Da Zhou Tian*) within the body.

The point of all these techniques is simply to lead your Qi through your Qi channels in a forceful way that thereby improves these circulatory routes by eliminating any obstructions within those major Qi channels.

A different type of breathing practice focuses on opening up the Qi routes within selected body parts rather than meridian pathways. For these you inhale and then hold your Qi energy in various regions of your body as long as possible, while remaining relaxed, and then exhale slowly after you are unable to retain the air any longer. You should practice this for your *dantian*; your entire pelvic region (including its internals, sacrum and genitals); your legs; your arms; your torso; your neck and throat; and your head.

After gaining proficiency in holding your Qi at various points within your pelvis, starting at your sacrum you should progressively inhale and hold your Qi at higher and higher points along your spine. Coming to your shoulder blades, you should hold it at each shoulder in turn. You should also hold it at your throat, heart, nose, inside of your mouth (including your teeth, gums, back of throat and palate), nose, eyes and the entire head.

You must repeat this technique proceeding downwards from head to toes, gaining control over it. You take in the air and hold your breath and your Qi energy in the various limbs of your body and at other vital spots by raising it repeatedly from the chest region and *dantian* alternately.

In advanced stages of martial arts practice you train to unify each muscle movement with your breathing, Qi and especially the Qi of your *dantian* so that you can draw energy from this region. As one type of training practice, martial artists often practice the *Kai-He Shou Shi* (Open-Unite Hands Posture), which is also known as the "Moving Qi Among Three Points" exercise, in order to learn how to compact and direct their Qi from their *dantian*. For this exercise, during a standing posture you mentally lead the Qi from your *dantian* to the center of both palms that are held slightly facing one another. Inhaling, your Qi is drawn back to your *dantian* and exhaling your Qi moves to reside in the palms. This is a practice used to pulsate Qi back and forth so that it becomes ready to move beyond your body.

After doing this several minutes, you must concentrate on a point directly in front of the center of both palms, which are facing each other. The center of the palms and this point are to form an imaginary circle that is to be filled with Qi like an energy ball. Using concentrated breathing, you stir the Qi within your *dantian*, and then direct that Qi into your palms upon exhalation. Continuing the exhalation you must direct the Qi beyond the palms into the center of the imagined circle.

Once the Qi reaches the circle's center it expands and presses upon the three points that hold it back so that it does not move beyond the circle. You actually try to push Qi out from your body so that you feel this Qi collecting. Subsequent breaths are used to gather more Qi within the circle so that you can start sensing its density, which is either light or heavy. As you continue inhaling and exhaling, the three points should seek expansion from the Qi compacting and condensing between them, but it should always remain within their boundaries. In this type of training you are learning to make your Qi heavy, which is compacted Qi that can be directed at opponents when fighting, and you are sourcing your Qi from your *dantian*.

All sorts of practices like this are available in the martial arts. Some are considered secret, some are only transmitted by a master to qualified pupils, some are readily available from ancient books, but the entire purpose is to help you purify your Qi channels, make Qi flow more efficient, and help you develop the ability to manipulate your Qi.

ABDOMINAL BREATH TRAINING

In order to use your mind to lead your Qi effectively, you must first learn to regulate your breathing. This is one of the purposes behind an initial emphasis on pranayama and *qi-gong* practice. Thoughts can affect your breathing and breathing can affect your thoughts. Breathing can also affect your Qi and thoughts can affect your Qi. Therefore, all sorts of practice methods have been developed using your thoughts or breathing to affect the Qi within your body. These interrelationships are the secret.

There are many different types of breathing for many different purposes, but for attaining a clear and open mind your breathing must become slow and smooth. This is why you practice alternate nostril breathing and pranayama to open up your Qi channels. Once you breath correctly, your mind will become better able to lead your Qi effectively.

Buddhism teaches abdominal breathing, or *Zhen Hu Xi,* as a method for naturally opening your Qi channels. When you inhale you normally expand your abdomen (lower *dantian*), and when you exhale your abdomen normally contracts. This breathing pattern can be used for leading your Qi to circulate in your primary Qi channels. During sitting meditation practice, for instance, you can perform breathing exercises where upon inhalation you expand your abdomen and upon exhalation, when the abdomen contracts, you can lead your Qi to different areas of your body. For instance, upon inhaling (with eyes closed) you can guide your Qi up your spine, and when exhaling you can guide the Qi into your palms and fingers. This is a way to open the Qi channels within your spine as well as your arms, hands and fingers.

Taoist breathing, which is frequently used in the martial arts, uses reverse abdominal breathing, or *Fan Fu Hu Xi.* With Taoist breathing, you contract your abdomen when you inhale and expand it as you exhale. You can use this breathing method to practice expanding your Qi to your skin or other body regions. As you exhale, you should send your Qi into your muscles, limbs and the surface of your skin, and on inhalation you draw your breath into the center of your bones.

Both the Buddhist and Taoist breathing practices can and should be practiced at idle times of the day such as when watching television or waiting for something. While it may seem as if you are not making progress in any way, the cumulative effect of such practices over time cannot be underestimated.

There is also Wim Hof breathing, which is a type of controlled rhythmical power breathing (hyperventilation) followed by a period of retention. It is used to increase mental clarity and improve general athletic performance. To practice, you take in a powerful breath that fully fills your lungs. Then you almost immediately breathe out, but not forcefully. This brings a lot of oxygen into your system because it is similar to hyperventilation. You repeat this at a steady pace thirty to forty times, which may produce some harmless tingling sensations in your fingers and feet as well as some light-headedness. After completing thirty to forty cycles of this controlled hyperventilation, on the last inhalation of this series you take in one final inhalation as deeply as possible, and let it out completely. Then, you stop breathing and hold your lungs empty for as long as possible until you feel the urge to breath again. When a strong urge to breathe occurs, draw in one big recovery breath to fill your lungs, chest and belly. Hold this recovery breath for around 15–20 seconds and then let it go. In summary, you have controlled hyperventilation, done in three to six sets of 30-40 breaths, and on the last breath of each set you exhale and hold for 1-3 minutes before taking a recovery breath that you hold for 15-20 seconds. If you so desire you can repeat the recovery breath three to four times. The Wim Hof breathing produces a calm state conducive to meditation, so can be performed just prior to meditation practice.

There is also Ah-breathing, which is a quick pre-meditation breath routine that few know about. It is breath work that you perform just prior to sitting down in meditation practice (where the target is to quiet your mind) and is used because it instantly silences your mind. To do this you breathe in through your nose and then exhale slowly through your mouth three to five times in succession. The breathing is natural with one exception. Every out-breath of exhalation should be as if you are letting go of every possible thought or concern bothering you in life, and you silently say "Ahhh" when you do this. You exhale slowly from your mouth with the exhalation being about twice as long as your inhalation, and on the exhalation you let go of all the tension, concerns and worries that are burdening your mind. After you do this several times in a row and feel "now life is perfect," you can instantly enter into a quiet meditative state that would not normally be possible without this bit of preparatory work.

ZEN WALKING

When doing natural walking, or what is called "Zen walking" between meditation sessions where you are taught to focus on body awareness, you can practice different types of breath work and Qi manipulations as well. You should always practice *qi-gong* and breathing methods while walking that will push your Qi throughout your body to help open up meridian pathways. These exercises will gradually improve the ease by which your Qi can circulate throughout your body.

Most practitioners during Zen walking waste their time because they simply walk and don't perform breath work or any other Qi practice while moving. Practicing breathing methods or exercises to circulate your Qi at those times *is far more important than focusing on awareness as you walk*, and this focus on Qi can be considered the true practice of Buddhist *anapana* (breath awareness practice).

One marvelous way to improve Zen walking is to hold your arms in *baguazhang* (or other meridian-stimulating) positions and concentrate on the Qi flow within them while walking since that activates particular Qi meridians, and while doing so concentrate on breathing that moves your Qi energy through the meridians being stimulated (exercised) by the arm postures. To make the practice even more productive, you can also simultaneously visualize the meridians within your flesh that you are concentrating upon. If a Qi meridian is associated with an internal organ system, you can further improve your results dramatically by also holding onto the emotions relevant to that organ since this will further stimulate the Qi of that meridian.

During Zen walking done in this way (or any walking routine where you practice these methods), after a certain length of time – perhaps because the proctor says "switch" – you would change *baguazhang* (or other) arm patterns and therefore work on sequentially opening different meridians one by one.

It is good that the Zen school has at least this minor form of walking exercise because it is unhealthy to practice only sitting meditation or seated forms of *qi-gong*. Basically, your Qi can become stagnant through inactivity. Static stationary practices must always be accompanied by movement exercises, which is why Bodhidharma taught *Yi Jin Jing* exercises to the Shaolin monks. He wanted to help improve their health since they were neglecting their physical bodies, which is a common mistake made by monks and nuns in the Zen tradition.

Taoist master Zhang Sanfeng also developed *taijiquan* as a form of discipline complementary to meditation practice that would improve the physique, help the inner organs, and promote health as well as inner Qi development. The Korean Zen (Seon) Buddhists also developed *Sunmudo*, which is a form of martial arts that also incorporates yoga with meditation as a road to enlightenment. Many martial arts schools depend upon meditation for skills development just as meditation schools should be paired with the martial arts. *Akido* in Japan, Judo, Korean *taekwondo* and Vietnamese boxing are among the many eastern martial arts that use meditation as a means of attaining the highest levels of skill.

As to the Zen school, it should put a greater emphasis on exercise and movement principles in its training techniques through simple exercise routines like this *that also develop your inner Qi body*. After all, you must cultivate both life (Qi) and consciousness to succeed in the Tao and attain enlightenment. If the Zen tradition would adopt the soft martial arts and yoga as part of its mandatory training system then far more people would attain enlightenment. As to the mundane benefits this would produce as a form of preventative medicine for health maintenance, this goes without saying.

Over the centuries, many breathing sets have been created based on similar principles and therefore have similar forms. If you understand the principles you can construct your own. For instance, a popular and powerful martial arts breathing practice is simply to guide your Qi up your spine while inhaling, and then guide your Qi into your palms and fingers upon exhalation. The method is as simple as that.

By the practice of such breathing methods and pranayama practices (which will add power to our breath), and in connection with meditation, you will not only get better at martial arts striking abilities but purify your body's and Qi channels in preparation for *nei-gong* and the higher martial arts attainments that require tremendous power within the body.

7
CULTIVATING THE BODY'S QI IN SECTIONS

Fixing your Qi for a long time at various points within your body, and holding visualizations at those points or simply washing them with Qi, is one way to cultivate the entire Qi of your body in sequence.

If you partition your body into logically defined sections such as torso segments, body cavities, limbs, muscles, glands, internal organs, bones, etcetera then you can then work at cultivating your entire body by using your mind-guided Qi to wash all such areas one by one. Eventually you can link the purified Qi of all the body segments into one undivided whole and thereby create permanent power. Power becomes permanent after sufficient Qi cultivation to cleanse and unite your internal energy, whereas force (the usage of power) is temporary.

There are several ways to work on purifying and transforming the Qi of body sections. Using your mind you can try to feel the Qi of an entire region by concentrating on internal sensations within it, and simply hold onto the feeling of the "energy" or "substance" of that section. You might also mentally wash it with a visualization of bright sunlight or moonlight.

You can use your mind to push your Qi energy throughout all your various body parts and sections. You can ultimately guide it to wash all the sections of your body and their interior components. It takes time to learn how to perfect mind-guided movements of your Qi. Bodhidharma's "marrow cleansing" technique within the *Xi Sui Jing* follows this principle as applied to bones.

You can also recite mantras or *bija* sounds on body sections, or as if from within body sections. Furthermore, you can recite *bija* sounds on top of strategic *bindus* (points) such as acupuncture points, pressure points, *Dim mak* points, or marma points. Reciting a sound as if at a point or upon a point will stimulate all the Qi around it, thus serving as a form of Qi cultivation.

While performing such practices you can try to arouse positive (Yang) or negative (Yin) emotions within yourself in order to stimulate the Yin Qi or Yang Qi of your body, and in particular the Qi within that section. Emotions can used to stimulate, arouse, excite, energize, invigorate, and transform the Qi within your body. Martial artists and yogis tend to think that you should only cultivate your Yang Qi, but your Yin Qi must be cultivated and purified as well.

Here are some classical ways to partition the body into sections so that you can work on transforming the Qi within each segment.

TWO SECTIONS:

Left side, right side; Top and bottom; Front and back; Up the spine and down the front of the body through the *du mai* and *ren mai*; Up the spine and down the spine; Alimentary canal (the tube from mouth to anus) and everything surrounding it – these are various ways of partitioning the body into two parts.

The Buddhist and Hindu sutras recommend that you use the sounds of Om or Ah or Ram, or recite the Rah-Vah (also Ram-Vam) mantra, within the different body sections in order to transform the Qi of your underlying energetic nature. This work will help to improve Qi flow throughout your body, which is essential for the highest level of martial arts proficiency. Leading your Qi upwards or downwards in your body, to the left or right, in a clockwise or counterclockwise direction, and so on are all ways of moving your Qi internally to wash your tissues.

Traditionally the right side of your body is considered Yang, and the left side Yin. The traditional cultivation method of Buddhist Arhats is to concentrate on feeling heat and fire on one side of the body (that is envisioned with the color red), and feeling cooling water on the other side (which is envisioned with the color blue or white). After sufficient practice, the hotness and coolness are switched to the other side of the body. This is practiced within the top and the bottom (from the waist to the feet) sections of the body, and for the left and right sides of the body.

This is essentially the Taoist practice of *Li* and *Kan*, which is working to purify the Yin Qi and Yang Qi of your body. Yogis and the supreme martial artists use a variety of methods to cultivate the Yin and Yang energies of their bodies. Rather than fire and water, you can practice feeling the energy of the sun on one side of the body and the energy of the moon on the other, and then switch them. Another martial arts practice is to feel that one half of the body is empty while the other is heavy, and then to switch sides again with those feelings.

THREE SECTIONS:

Head with neck and arms, chest and middle torso, thighs and legs to feet; Head and neck, arms and chest and trunk to pelvic waist, legs and feet; Head, chest and arms to waist, thighs and legs to feet; Backside of the body running upwards, front side of the body running downwards, inner core of digestive organs – these are some of the many ways to partition the body into three parts.

Om-Ah-Hung, Om-Ah-Hum, Om-So-Hum, Om-Aum-Hum and Hreem-Shreem-Kleem are some of the three-syllable mantras used to stimulate and purify the Qi in each of the three body sections. Each syllable of these mantras is to be recited within a different segment of the body so as to vibrate the Qi within it.

For instance, Samantabhadra's mantra of "Om-Ah-Hung" is used extensively in the Esoteric school of Buddhism. To use this mantra to transform your body's Qi quickly you would recite "Ah" while trying the feel the Qi of your head, neck and arms. This is the upper part of your body according to one partitioning scheme. You would then recite "Ah" while trying to feel the Qi within your arms and torso. This is the middle section of your body. You would then recite "Hung" or "Hum" while trying to feel the energy in the lower section of your body from your waist down to your feet. Other three-syllable mantras are available to be used in a similar manner.

FOUR SECTIONS:

Head, neck and arms, arms and chest (middle torso), lower abdomen and pelvis, legs and feet; Upper left quadrant of the body, upper right quadrant of the body, lower left quadrant of the body, lower right quadrant of the body – these are just some of the ways to partition the body into fours.

Om-Ah-Vah-Lah, Om-Hreem-Shreem-Kleem, and Sah-Rah-Vah-Nah are some four-part mantras that apply for the head, chest, abdomen, and waist to legs. One can also use the five-syllable mantra Ah-Vi-Ra-Hum-Kham where the first four syllables are apportioned to four sections of the body while the final "Kham" should shake the Qi of the entire body in total, or just be used on the spine.

FIVE SECTIONS:

While the body can easily be partitioned into five sections, your Qi can be partitioned into five categories as well.

According to the five Vayus (winds or Qi-types) principles of Hinduism, our head and arms correspond to the ascending Qi called *Udana*; the region of the chest with lungs and heart corresponds to *Prana*; the mid-trunk of body containing digestive organs corresponds to *Samana* Qi; the lower abdomen and pelvis corresponds to the Qi called *Apana;* the entire body is pervaded by *Vyana* that is especially located in the legs to the feet. Some yoga schools differ on this attribution scheme, so this is just one of the many ways to partition the body into five parts. Om-Ah-Vah-Lah-Hum is one of the many five-syllable mantras you can use to cultivate your Qi in these five body sections. Another is Om-Ah-Vah-Rah-Hum.

Besides the five Prana, martial artists are often taught to evoke different internal feelings in their training that correspond to different flavors of Qi. They must not only learn how to make their Qi surge, ebb, be stored and be guided to wherever their mind directs, but must be able to change the quality of that Qi. The quality, flavor, feeling or nature of your Qi is often represented by the characteristic temperament of an animal such as a snake, monkey, tiger, dragon, crane and so forth. Thus, students are sometimes taught to practice the spirit and movement of an animal in order to master particular movements as well as transform the quality of their Qi.

Similarly, you can also recognize for each of the five elements – earth, water, fire, wind and space – a different type of Qi energy within your body. Each type of element Qi can be purified through a different type of Qi training. In fact, you can practice Qi purification exercises for your Yin and Yang Qi, the five elements of your body, and other partitioning schemes that segment Qi into different types. To do this, you must focus on feeling that type of energy within your entire body, perhaps by first stimulating it, and hold onto that Qi sensation.

Earth represents the solidity of your body, is especially felt within your flesh and bones, and is cultivated by imagining that your body becomes solid, heavy, yellow earth. Often masters teach students to merge with a boulder, mountain or wall that they train next to (or feel its energy) in order to help them cultivate their earth element Qi.

Water represents fluidity and the Yin Qi of the body, which is 70% water, and is cultivated by imagining that your body's entirety becomes cool blue water, or simply white in color. Often masters teach students to train next to a lake whose energy they might feel or try to merge with in order that they cultivate their water element Qi or Yin Qi.

Fire represents the heat and Yang Qi of your body, and is cultivated by imagining that your body becomes a raging fire. Wind represents just the Qi or vital energy of your body, which is often referred to as the wind element, and is cultivated by imagining that your body loses its structure and is just a matrix of coursing energy everywhere. Space represents the ultimate nature of your body that is empty like space, and is cultivated by imagining (and feeling) that your body becomes like an empty sack, or is abandoned entirely and becomes universal empty space.

A practitioner should progress through these contemplations one-by-one to purify the Qi of their body and end them by abandoning all notions to rest their mind in emptiness by imagining they become empty space.

The *Visuddhimagga*, or great treatise of Theravada Buddhist cultivation written by Buddhaghosa, has teachings on cultivating the five elements within the body through concentrations, called *kasina* meditations, but these lessons are incomprehensible without this information.

In the martial arts, special attention must be paid to each of the elements within five elements cultivation. For instance, the earth element represents an integral combination of all the elements together (they all exist within the earth element), and is the embodiment of both Yin and Yang essences combined together. For martial arts it is important to practice the earth element cultivation method of feeling rooted in your feet so that you develop firmness in your stepping. You practice feeling the earth element below your feet united with the Yin Qi in your foot. Or, you can practice sinking your Qi into your legs and feet as if the entire Earth empties its weight into your shape, and then mix this feeling in your feet with the Qi of the Earth. When martial artists practice heaviness in the legs or feet in order to develop this firmness, they must make sure that the feeling doesn't transform into sluggishness.

SIX SECTIONS:

Heart, lungs, stomach, liver, kidneys, and triple warmer – this is one of the ways to partition the body into six internal organs.

The organs correspond to the Taoist six healing sounds Haa (heart), Szz (lungs), Hoo (stomach), Shoo (liver), Foo (kidneys), and Shee (the three sections of the upper, middle and lower warmer). Different traditions will use different sounds for the organs, and the proper sounds are those that help you feel or move the Qi of the organs. While practicing, you can try to feel the positive or negative emotions associated with each organ.

SEVEN SECTIONS:

The body can be partitioned into seven sections using a symbolism of "seven chakras," which corresponds to body sections delineated by spinal vertebrae and their nerves. The top chakra is the thousand-petalled *Sahasrara* crown chakra that represents our brain with all its neurons and nerves. Its nerves can be seen in DTI diffusion tensor images, and those pictures should be used to guide any internal Qi rotation practices that you perform to "wash your brain" and help open up its Qi channels. This will result in higher mental quietness, clarity, and speedier reflex responses.

Incidentally, the brain is Kamadhenu, the wish-fulfilling cow of Hinduism and Buddhism (that becomes the Sphinx of Egyptian mythology and Chimera of Greek mythology)[8], and the Qi channels within it must be opened through countless Qi washings. The Tibetan Windhorse (Lung-Ta) that carries the wish-fulfilling jewel of enlightenment, which is the brain stem, is also a symbol of Kamadhenu and the brain as well. As stated, Kamadhenu has its equivalent in the Sphinx of ancient Egypt who could ask questions of humans since the Sphinx symbolizes the brain. The hairs of the Sphinx represent the nerves or Qi channels in the brain, its wings represent the two brain lobes, the four paws represent its four sections and the tail of the Sphinx represents our spinal cord.

The Lamassu or Sadu of Mesopotamia (Sumerian and Akkadian mythology), which looks like the Sphinx (and Kamadhenu), also represents our brain. Further, the strange creature Navagunjara that the warrior Arjuna meets in the Hindu epic *Mahabharata* represents our brain as well, which is a fact unknown to scholars. The Greek Chimera also represents the brain

---

[8] See *Nyasa Yoga* and *Buddha Yoga* for details.

through its many lion hairs that are the brain nerves, its two wings that are the two brain lobes with neurons (feathers), the two goat horns that are the two protruding nerve bundles that ascend upwards from the spinal cord, the snake tail that represents the spine and cobra head-shaped coccyx, and its fire represents the *kundalini* energy necessary to transform it.

The two-part "third eye" *Ajna* chakra is our brain stem that has conjoined left and right, Yin and Yang sections like the Shiva-Parvati *Ardhanarishvara*. This is the "muddy pellet" of Taoism, and the hump on the back of Kamadhenu the wish-fulfilling cow. Its two horns represent two ascending spinal nerve bundles that reach from the spine to the top of the head. The great sage yogi Gorasknath named Kamadhenu's four teats Ambika (mother), Lambika (eyes at the summit), Ghantika (sound) and Talika (clapping) in order to represent two nodes of the superior colliculus and inferior colliculus in the brainstem that process visual and auditory information.

The sixteen-petalled *Vishuddha* throat chakra is the set of C1, C2, ... C8 cervical vertebrae and their surrounding tissues of the neck, face and upper chest ruled by the nerves extending out of those vertebrae.

The twelve-petalled *Anahata* heart chakra corresponds to the regions of the body controlled by the T1 through T12 thoracic vertebrae nerves.

The ten-petalled *Manipura* navel (solar plexus) chakra corresponds to the section of the body served by the left and right nerves protruding from the L1, L2, ... L5 lumbar spinal vertebrae, and represents the "*hara*" of Japanese martial arts or lower *dantian* of Chinese medicine.

The *Svadhisththana* sacral chakra corresponds to the sacrum. This chakra is often represented by a crocodile because rough crocodile scales remind people of the bony protrusions of the sacrum, and its six petals refer to the six nerves protruding from each side of vertebrae S1, S2, S3, S4, S5, and C0.

The four-petalled *Muladhara* root chakra, often symbolized by a four-sided square, a four-legged elephant or a four-armed deity, symbolizes your pelvic girdle muscles along with your asshole, perineum and genitals (male genitalia are symbolized by the head of an elephant). The major muscles around the perineum form a square of four sides because seen from below two ischiocavernosus muscles form a corner of the square, the diagonal is the superficial transverse perineal muscle, and the ileococcygeous muscle forms the rest of the square. Hence, mandalas have four sides to represent this area of our torso, and Hindu deities commonly have four arms to represent the power of this region as well. In other words, the four-petalled chakra just represents the bottommost section of our torso.

Power-possessing Hindu deities are shown with four arms to represent the muscles of this square that is the primal source or basis of power for all the muscles above. The center of the square contains the perineum or *huiyin* DU-1 acupuncture point, which is the *haidi* or "bottom of the ocean" from which Sun Wu-Kong retrieved his staff. Thus the pelvic region in general is usually symbolized by the root chakra together with the sacral chakra, which are sometimes together represented by an elephant (who symbolizes great power). The Goddess Ganga, who is symbolized as having four arms and riding a crocodile in the Ganges River, also symbolizes the pelvis, sacrum and spine together. The Ganges River she rides upon represents Qi ascending the *du mai* into the brain.

All of these sections can be washed with Qi that can be vibrated by traditional *bija* sounds recited within them. The *Mahavairocana Sutra* of Buddhism and *Yoga Yajnavalkya* recommend the same set of sounds to help wash each body part with Qi, which is called the "disposition of letters" or "disposition of syllables." However, these are not to be taken as definitive. The best mantra sounds to use are those that vibrate the Qi within the section being concentrated on, and sometimes you can find sounds to do this that have not been recorded in ancient scriptures. If a tone vibrates the Qi channels within certain sections of the body, it is considered a *bija* or root sound for that body part and you can use it.

Each school recommends different *bija* sounds to help resonate the Qi within separate body parts, and that information is often only transmitted in mantras. Sometimes a mantra is designed to vibrate the Qi of your body, and sometimes it is designed to ask the assistance of a Buddha, deity or Immortal to use their own Qi to work on purifying the Qi of your body segments and cleanse the underlying subtle body within them. You might inquire of a master as to which mantra may work best for you.

EIGHT SECTIONS:

Another torso partitioning scheme[9] of eight sections can be made using seven fascial meridians or meridians of latitude called "bands" that segment the body into eight parts. While the seven sectional scheme based on chakras is delineated based on nerves and spinal vertebrae, this sectioning scheme is based on fascial planes within the body, and hence is more relevant to the Qi flow inside us.

The first meridian is the eye band that is a horizontal plane starting from the bridge of the nose and running to the back of the skull. The section of the body delineated by going upwards thus contains the eyes and the brain. The chin band is the angular line formed by the bottom of the chin slicing upwards to back of the skull. This band to the eye band contains the bottom region of the head including the nasal cavity, teeth, tongue, palate and cerebellum. As with all other body structures, these parts must all be washed over and over again by revolving your Qi inside them in many diverse ways. The collar band is a strap running around the bottom of the neck centered on the clavicle (collar bone) and continuing towards the back on the upper border of the shoulder blade (scapula) ending at the junction of the cervical and thoracic vertebrae. The body region delineated contains the neck with thyroid gland. The chest band is the area just below the nipples running horizontally as a band around the body. This band running upwards to the collar meridian contains the heart, lungs, thymus gland, shoulders and arms. The abdomen (belly or umbilical) band starts at the belly button and then wraps horizontally around the body. This band upwards to the chest band contains the internal organs of stomach, pancreas, spleen, liver, gall bladder and kidneys. The inguinal band runs across the lower abdomen starting at the back of the buttocks and running atop the pelvic bones until falling at their front, slightly dipping downwards,

---

[9] Dr. Louis Schultz and Dr. Rosemary Feitis discovered these horizontal bands within the body's myofascia, which are thickening in the deep layers of fascia and connective tissue. See *Anatomy Trains* by Thomas Myers for illustrations.

thus taking the shape of an inverted arch. From the inguinal band to the umbilical meridian are the bulk of the intestines. The pubic band extends from the public bone (pubic symphysis) in the front of the body across the groin to the bottom of the buttocks in the back. From the public band to the inguinal band above it is the region containing the sacrum and coccyx as well as the genitals. The lowest section of the body below the pubic band contains the legs and feet. This section starts from the public band that stretches like a gentle arch from the pelvic bone to the bottom of the buttocks, thus defining the beginning of the legs.

HUNDREDS OF BONES BECOME ONE BODY:

Using the white skeleton visualization method of Buddhism, the hundreds of bones within your body can be sequentially washed clean by visualizing a bright shining light doing so, starting with your left big toe and working upwards bone by bone to the top of your head. When Shakyamuni Buddha taught this method of internal Qi work he said that a practitioner should always start with their feet and then progressively ascend upwards. Toes, feet, thighs, legs, pelvis, torso, arms, hands, fingers … you imagine that all the individual bones within you shine with a bright white light. You try to feel the Qi of the bones or wash their outer shape as you visualize them shining with bright energy. In other words, you don't just visualize the bones shining with bright light but should try to feel the shape of each bone, or wash each bone with Qi (including its marrow) as you would wash any other area of your body. The Qi of all your bones, limbs and appendages must be worked on to become more purified.

Next, the Qi of the cleansed bones (once they are all visualized within you as bight white in color) can be threaded together as a single unified whole. The Qi of discrete bones and body parts must achieve unification, the divided must combine. In *neijia*, you must combine the Qi of every part of your body into one whole. After washing each individual bone with bright white light and Qi, you then thread together all the bones into the feeling of being one unified body of Qi.

The practice involves truly *feeling* the Qi of your individual bones (feeling the sensation of the shape of your bones within your limbs and torso) rather than just performing a mental visualization in your head that never actually touches the energy of the bones of your body. You must always cultivate the feeling of the bones inside your body, where they are, and should wash the shape of the bones, inside and out, with the energy of bright white light. When you proceed onto the next bone, all the previous bones are felt as continuing to shine with a bright light as when you left them.

Since the white skeleton visualization involves individually visualizing all the bones of your body as shining with a bright silvery light, or like sunshine, this is energizing to your body's Qi. Therefore sexual desire may arise. Ignore it. Since your skeleton stretches throughout your entire body and your muscles are draped upon it, it runs parallel to the flow of the major Qi channels within your body. All your muscles run along the shape of your skeleton, so by concentrating on your skeleton and filling it with bright Qi you will bring Qi to all those muscles as well as your bones. Unbeknownst to people, this method is then an equivalent to the martial arts practices of internal marrow cleansing.

After working on producing a complete brightly shining skeleton within you, which corresponds to feeling the Qi of your entire body, you then let go of this feeling of having a body and imagine that the bones turn into dust that disperses into space. Then you rest your mind in formlessness as if your body and mind were nothing but empty space. There is awareness, but since you abandon the feeling that you possess a body there is no reason for attachment to anything. Just remain in the conscious awareness of whatever is in the space around you that you can see or hear in your mind. None of it is anything you can touch or affect since you are just empty space that has consciousness. By having fully energized the Qi throughout your body and then abandoning the idea of possessing physical boundaries, unrestricted Qi flow will arise within you and you will sometimes experience a state of bliss.

This mental yoga exercise is of the nature of infinite awareness or infinite knowing where no *coarse* mind-objects objects are clung to, but of course the mind-stream still operates. This is the yoga of Patanjali, and is the *chit* (pure consciousness) of *sat-chit-ananda*. It is the "empty mind" of Buddhism where the mind is open, calm, peaceful, clear and relatively empty of the loud narrative we always have inside ourselves of a personal thought-stream. It is the pure consciousness or pristine awareness of Vedanta that is a state of mental equanimity or bliss. The mind is still an alert field of awareness enjoying the qualities of existence but it is not riddled with coarse thoughts.

So at the end of the practice you always imagine that your body disperses into emptiness and you let go of holding onto your thoughts while retaining the awareness of consciousness, which is how all Vajrayana methods must end. You don't want to become entrained with and entangled within thought-streams where you lose yourself and your independent perspective by becoming identified with your thoughts, nor cling to the internal sensations of Qi movements you have provoked. It is through detachment that your body can achieve an internal harmonious balance of Qi on its own without thought interference.

At this stage you should ignore all the sensations of your body and avoid clinging to internal Qi movements because in this stage of "empty mind" your Qi has been stimulated and is now moving. It is through the active movement of Qi that it can dissolve internal circulation problems so that the body's energy can come together as a unified whole.

Sitting, reclining, walking around, you can now practice feeling the Qi of your entire body as one single unit, like an inflated balloon without internal divisions, or like an empty sack. At a higher level you can abandon the body feeling entirely if it fills with Qi completely.

Since any type of body still has a skin or limit to it, you should try to forget the sensations of the body entirely and become just empty space. This will help your internal Qi flow tremendously for the martial arts, and is one of the ways to improve your practice of motionless standing postures when your mind should remain tranquil without giving birth to incessant ripples of thought. You just *be*. Eventually you should extend the feeling of being an empty body even unto the eyes, ears, nose, teeth, penis, scrotum, breasts, fingers and toes while you resist attaching to any Qi sensations since you are practicing "having no body at all."

The white skeleton visualization practice, as well as Bodhidharma's bone marrow washing *nei-gong*, are techniques that martial artists normally use to transform the Qi within all the bones of their body. There are over thirty different versions of the basic white skeleton practice.

At the start of this practice technique, prior to imagining a single bone, you have the option of first stimulating your body's Yin Qi by arousing the emotions of revulsion and disgust. You can do this by imagining that your body passes through several repulsive stages of decay before the flesh drops away to reveal its bones. Sitting in a lotus meditation posture, you progressively visualize that your body disgustingly decomposes and passes through the stages of being a (1) a swollen corpse, (2) discolored bluish corpse, (3) festering corpse, (4) fissured corpse, (5) gnawed corpse, (6-7) dismembered or hacked and scattered corpse, (8) bleeding corpse, and (9) worm-eaten corpse. In other words, you imagine your body progressively decomposing so that disgust mentally arises within you in order to arouse your Yin Qi. Then what is sitting there is just a set of bones, and you begin to make them shine individually as per the previous instructions.

An alternative to this Yin Qi prelude is to imagine *joyfully* offering away all your body's flesh to any ghostly beings to whom you might owe debts, and then begin the white bone visualization. You imagine stripping away the flesh from your body to reveal the bones, which is grabbing the Qi of your muscles, and doing this for your complete body. The emotion of joy during the stripping and offering away, which you can also arouse by thinking that you are purifying your muscles, is meant to raise your Yang Qi.

Thus the practice combines the stimulation of Yin Qi and Yang Qi, and then works on brightly stimulating the Yang Qi within your bones, which are difficult to transform because they are the densest earth element of the body. At the very end of one session of practice you will have cultivated the Qi of all your bones, and thus your entire body, at which time you should try to feel it as a single unit. Accomplishing this, you then should ignore all physical sensations by resting your mind in emptiness as if you were only empty space, and let your Qi move on its own in order that it opens up any Qi pathways within you that it can.

ONE SECTION – A SINGLE WHOLE

A similar technique exists for the objective of cultivating the entire Qi of your body as a single unit. For this visualization method you imagine that at the level of your navel there is a large red lotus flower inside you pointing upwards that is burning with fiery flames. Sitting in a meditation posture, you imagine that the fiery flames gradually engulf your body turning it red in color. You simultaneously try to stimulate the energy everywhere inside you while you feel great joy and elation at burning away all body impurities.

The fire from the bright red lotus should be imagined extending upwards through your body and protruding out the center of your head. The reason you visualize the flames protruding out of the top of your head is because concentrating on a point above your body will help to draw Qi upwards, and thus this visualization will draw your Qi through the two ascending branches of your cranial spinal nerves that reach to the top of your head.

These left and right nerve bundles that branch upwards out of the spine are symbolized as antlers or horns in most cultural traditions. The horns of Yamantaka, horns of Isis holding a sun above her head, wisdom horns of Moses, the two pointed ears of an owl that represents wisdom, the antlers on stags, and the two long feathers protruding from Sun Wu-Kong's headdress are symbols of these two spinal nerve branches within the brain that can be purified when the ascending Qi of your body runs through them. All the nerves in your brain must be similarly purified, and after sufficient transformation this will help you attain great clarity and the quickest reaction speeds in martial arts.

At the level of your heart, you must also imagine an inverted lotus flower inside you that is bright red in color. Thus you have a red lotus flower in your lower abdomen burning with a fire blazing upwards, and a red lotus flower at the level of the heart that is turned upside down. You should imagine that fiery flames flow between these two lotus flowers, making the trunk of your body energized with fiery red Qi, and during this bouncing back and forth you should entertain a joyous excitedness that extends to your entire body that is turning bright red in color. So there is a fire flowing back and forth between the *dantian* and heart lotuses, and it is energizing your body by making it feel hot with excited happy energy.

You should practice being euphoric, elated, happy, joyful or thrilled when performing this exercise because these emotions will, in addition to the fire visualization, help you generate Yang Qi during the process, so you use this method to stir up your positive Yang Qi with a fervor. The principle to remember is that emotions stimulate sensations inside your body, and those sensations are energetic in nature. Hence they can be used to move your Qi and change its tonal qualities. You should actually try to *stimulate and feel* the energy moving everywhere inside you, while holding onto positive energetic emotion (such as happiness), in order to open up all your body's Qi channels using this method.

Imagining that you are fiery red in color from head to toe and full of Yang Qi (fire) energy, you then need to soak in the energetic feelings that result from this imagination, feeling the energy extending everywhere inside your body, and then imagine that your entire body eventually turns into glowing red embers because it is being burned by the fire. Energy is flowing everywhere within you.

After you visualize your entire body as filled with this fire energy, and you are nearing the time that you want to end the practice session, imagine that your body turns into red glowing embers. Once that visualization is completed, imagine that a strong wind blows off all the embers and ashes. Next, imagine that a heavy rain falls from above washing all the ashes away.

This is like the final phase of the white skeleton visualization where you imagine that your body turns into dust that blows away to leave behind just empty space. However, in this Qi purification exercise, you imagine that after the ashes blow away your body remains sitting there but is now transparent and crystal clean. It is pure and transparent like crystal, but empty in the sense of not being solid anymore. It is transparent and intangible.

When this is achieved, you then let go of all the imagining and rest your mind in empty space just as you did for the white skeleton visualization. By being like empty space you let everything arise within your mind without attachment since you now don't have a body because you are empty space. Be at peace and let your Qi arise in that state and start moving about to open up Qi channels without any guidance on your part.

Similar to this is yet another practice, called the Bhaisajya Visualization, based on the Medicine Buddha of Buddhism. Those who practice the Medicine Buddha sadhana will sit in a lotus meditation posture and imagine that their body, inside and out, becomes a peaceful whole that is a cooling royal blue, sky blue, or lapis lazuli in color. They try to feel the Qi of their flesh and imagine that it becomes blue in color, and cool in temperature. Then, they begin to imagine that it begins to radiate a flawless purity of brilliant light rays far and wide that shine forth to illuminate infinite, countless boundless realms across the galaxies. They have the option of projecting coolness outward into space, or transforming the coolness into warmth when doing so.

Yet another single body Qi cultivation technique is the "Duck Egg" or "Soma Cream" visualization transmitted from Japanese Mountain Master Hakuyu to Zen Master Hakuin Ekaku. The method: "Imagine that a lump of soft butter, pure in colour and fragrance and the size and shape of a duck egg, is suddenly placed on the top of your head. As it begins to slowly melt, it imparts an exquisite sensation, moistening and saturating your head within and without. It continues to ooze down, moistening your shoulders, elbows, and chest; permeating lungs, diaphragm, liver, stomach, and bowels; moving down the spine through the hips, pelvis, and buttocks.

"At that point, all the congestions that have accumulated within the five organs and six viscera, all the aches and pains in the abdomen and other affected parts, will follow the heart as it sinks downward into the lower body. As it does, you will distinctly hear a sound like that of water trickling from a higher to a lower place. It will move lower down through the lower body, suffusing the legs with beneficial warmth, until it reaches the soles of the feet, where it stops.

"The student should then repeat the contemplation. As his vital energy flows downward, it gradually fills the lower region of the body, suffusing it with penetrating warmth, making him feel as if he were sitting up to his navel in a hot bath filled with a decoction of rare and fragrant medicinal herbs that have been gathered and infused by a skilled physician.

"Inasmuch as all things are created by the mind, when you engage in this contemplation, the nose will actually smell the marvellous scent of pure, soft butter; your body will feel the exquisite sensation of its melting touch. Your body and mind will be in perfect peace and harmony. You will feel better and enjoy greater health than you did as a youth of twenty or thirty. At this time, all the undesirable accumulations in your vital organs and viscera will melt away. Stomach and bowels will function perfectly. Before you know it, your skin will glow with health. If you continue to practise the contemplation with diligence, there is no illness that cannot be cured, no virtue that cannot be acquired, no level of sagehood that cannot be reached, no religious practice that cannot be mastered. Whether such results appear swiftly or slowly depends only upon how scrupulously you apply yourself."[10]

Other than these, all of the previous sectioning schemes offered different ways of working on purifying the Qi of your body in segments instead of just a single whole that you attempt to cultivate entirely at once. As the segments become more purified, the Qi flow within them will become progressively free of more impediments and become smoother, which helps in yoga and the martial arts. All the segments of your body, regardless of how you partition it to make cultivation work easier, and regardless of what techniques you use, must be "washed" with Qi. At the same time, it is useful to hold onto specific emotions to specifically purify their Yin and Yang Qi.

In the internal martial arts, you must achieve unification. You must integrate the body and its energy into one seamless, continuous whole while the body's movements appear uninterrupted and graceful. The Qi of its individual parts must be continuously linked with very fine smoothness like the waves in a flowing stream.

You must practice martial arts to reach the stage where you cannot tell the difference between the end of one movement and start of another because

---

[10] *Wild Ivy: The Spiritual Autobiography of Zen Master Hakuin*, trans. by Norman Waddell (Shambhala Publications, Boston,1999), pp. 105-107.

the appearance is of one continuous graceful movement rather than a series of jerky movements stitched together. All the individual movements within a martial arts form should merely transform into the next. In yoga, the practice of *vinyasa* where you move from one *asana* (body position) to another by integrating your movements with breathing makes yoga a flowing exercise too rather than just a series of static exercises.

For the body partitioning practices to cultivate your inner Qi, you first work on cultivating the Qi of parts separately, then combine them into a single unity, and finally end the session by always resting in emptiness without the notion of having physical boundaries and without performing any Qi work led by your will. All the Qi of your body segments and parts should combine, the Qi with your muscles should combine, your mind and Qi should combine. From posture to posture, you want your internal power to be unbroken.

One particular problem in the martial arts is connecting the upper part of the body with the lower part so that their energies flow into each other as one seamless whole. In that way, the power from below can be accessed for striking moves made above.

The two halves of your body, upper and lower, are separated by your pelvis. The hips basically divide the top part of your body from the bottom part. There is actually a great temperature difference between the upper half of the body and the lower half, as easily seen in thermographic images, and the partitioning region or delineation line is the waist just above the pelvis, which is the region of transition. Another fact that can be seen from heat images of the body is that our weakest or poorest blood circulation occurs in our hands and feet, *which are therefore bottlenecks preventing the smooth flow of Qi everywhere else within the body!* This is why they need special attention through exercises designed to open up their Qi channels. The warmest part of the body is the spine, which is the easiest Qi pathway to open via various exercises (such as microcosmic breathing or visualization practices), and the root of the spine is the sacrum in the pelvis.

The complicated structure of bones, ligaments, tendons and muscles within the pelvis makes it hard for Qi to smoothly ascend and descend through this region. It is therefore hard to link your upper body with your lower body in the martial arts because of this internally complicated transitioning zone, whose structure makes it difficult to transmit power from your feet and hips to your striking. The *Taiji Classic* says, "The energy is rooted in the feet, develops in the legs and is directed by the waist." In martial arts and yoga you need to learn to control your upper and lower body as one by linking their energy into a unified whole. You want to be able to achieve the level where a wave of energy can arise from your toes, move upwards through your legs to your pelvis/waist and then into your hands and fingertips. You want to become able to spiral energy from your lower body on through the muscles of the pelvis to your arms for striking motions.

Your Qi everywhere therefore needs to be naturally connected, which is what you must work towards during all your years of practice. Your entire body with all its joints and extremities should become threaded together without the slightest break. All the muscles, ligaments, bones, organs and appendages must be integrated into having one unified Qi. Don't remain in a broken and non-continuous state but refine your one Qi. Perform yoga *asanas* to stretch all the muscles of your pelvis, especially those within it, and Qi exercises to lead your Qi through this region to also free it of internal circulatory impediments.

SPECIAL INSTRUCTIONS: HIPS AND GROIN

You must therefore perform lots of practice exercises that fully open up the hip region so that mechanical and energetic forces can proceed smoothly through the pelvis. Stretching all its muscles, tendons and ligaments will increase the energy flow within the pelvis so that the top and bottom of the body can become better connected. The great power available in this region is symbolized by the *Muladhara* four-petalled root chakra and *Svadhisththana* six-petalled sacral or sex chakra of yoga. But can you draw upon it?

Psychologically we have been trained to restrain our body's energies within this area because since youth we have been taught to hold back our shitting, pissing and farting. A number of psychological issues related to the restraint of energy flow through the pelvis are therefore imbedded within our psyche. The issue of sex involves pelvic restraints and inhibitions as well.

We don't exercise this area enough to stretch its muscles for better Qi flow, and we carry with us many psychological issues of energy restraint centered in this region, especially those concerned with sex. This creates localized internal restrictions that affect the smooth circulation of Qi from the lower to upper parts of the body.

Wild animals have no sexual psychological issues or inhibitions that block or impede the circulation of energy flow in their pelvis, but humans do. For yoga and the martial arts, men and women must train to eliminate unnecessary tension within their bodies, but they must not abandon the rules of sexual propriety adopted by society or the discipline of sexual restraint. As a general principle, however, you need to understand that all these various issues taken together hamper our energy flow through this area. You need to do exercises that stretch all the muscles in this region so that Qi circulation is maximized and the flow of power is unbroken.

For the highest levels of martial arts, we must exercise all the pelvic muscles in various ways so that our Qi can better pass through this region, and the energy of the upper half of the body can seamlessly connect with the lower half. We simply don't exercise this area enough through leg splits and other stretches. With enough of the proper type of stretching exercises, the energy of the upper half of your body will be able to better connect with the energy of the thighs, legs and feet, and the expression of power in the upper body can become one continuous circuit from below to above. When all motion adheres to the natural flow of Qi that has become smoother and freed of impediments then this will maximize the transmission of power. Power delivery will certainly increase, such as the flow of energy into a strike, if you clear that Qi flow conduit of its circulatory obstructions.

Among the many yoga exercises and stretches available, women should certainly practice kegel exercises for this region, which will also help with their sexual pleasure and performance. Men should practice *mula bandha*, *nauli kriya*, leg splits and other relevant hip and pelvic floor exercises. The martial arts have many relevant practices as well to stretch the various complicated structures within the hips and pelvis. Stretching the muscles within the pelvis will smoothen intra-pelvis Qi flow so that lower body power can be more fully expressed in the martial arts, and improving muscular flexibility in this region will help to decrease aggressive tendencies and reduce male problems with sexual desire.

Yoga master Tirumalai Krishnamacharya, who is the father of modern Yoga, recommended that Jalandhara Bandha Mudra, Shakti Calana Mudra, Ashwini Mudra, Pasini Mudra, Ardhabaddapadmapascimottan *asana*, Bakasan, Ekapada Sirsasana, Triviramasana and Sarvangasana be practiced to help activate the Yang Qi of your body, which yoga calls "*kundalini.*" Many of these *asanas* stretch the leg connections within the pelvic region so that its energy channels become unblocked or unwound. As a result, the untapped energy that resides in the pelvis can then flow without restrictions upwards through the body and the top of our torso can be linked with our legs and feet. Martial artists practice to unleash the energy of the pelvis, waist and leg muscles in order to transmit more power to their strikes, but they use different exercises to do so. Krishnamacharya's yoga exercises are highly beneficial for this purpose.

Taoism teaches several methods for cultivating and purifying the Qi channels of the genitals, which must be considered body "extremities" like the arms and legs. Men following Chinese exercises often hang weights from their scrotum to practice what they believe is a "transformation of Jing to Qi," but this dangerous weight-hanging exercise frequently leads to torn ligaments that require surgery. One surgeon told me that he has seen catastrophes from this practice. Thus this practice should be avoided as is also the case for the Aghori yoga practice of rolling one's penis on a stick to stretch it. Neither of these practices produces a transformation of Jing to Qi, nor do they decrease sexual desires.

In Taoism, the *Xi Sui Jing Qigong* teaches a method of massaging a man's scrotum and penis to improve their Qi flow, and this is superior to the dangerous and potentially debilitating exercise of hanging weights off the genitals. Yes, you do need to cultivate the Qi channels of the genitals for the highest levels of martial arts because their Qi flow is connected to the rest of the pelvis, and they should not become the bottleneck for fluent Qi flow through the pelvic region. Individuals tend to forget that the whole point of all these exercises is to improve the Qi circulation *everywhere within your body* for the martial arts objective of attaining the stage where you can feel that your physical nature is like a single body of energy. Yoga has this goal as well. Otherwise you cannot reach the stage of "no extremities" or "no body." If any body appendage or part goes uncultivated than this target objective cannot be achieved.

Therefore you must undertake Qi-based exercises for all the bones, ligaments, muscles, limbs, and even appendages of your body such as the genitals, ears, eyes, nose, tongue, teeth, fingers, toes and so forth. The cultivation of the Qi of these body parts is usually neglected by martial artists, even though pursuing iron shirt *gong-fu*, but those who have attained the highest stages of achievement understand the importance of fully cultivating the body everywhere. They undertake exercises to transform (purify) the Qi within their tongue, nose, teeth, ears, genitals, nails and hair because they all have Qi circulations linked to the rest of the body, and impediments to the Qi flow within these extremities constitute a bottleneck for the rate of Qi circulation in the rest of the body. One region that yogis and martial artists don't sufficiently work on is the groin area, which is often noted in Chinese *gong-fu* movies where a villain only exhibits "iron shirt" or "adamantine body" weakness in his private parts.

Two superior exercises for improving Qi circulation within the male genitalia are as follows, and are based on the Chinese practice of *Wo*. For each of these techniques a man should also learn how to circulate his Qi cylindrically and length-wise within his penis. Methods include mentally leading your Qi to rotate inside the tubular shaft of the penis along its length, or leading it up and down the length of the penis, or moving the Qi to cultivate just the left side or right side of the penis and scrotum together. In some exercises you breath into the left side of the penis and scrotum from the *dantian*, and then the right side alternately. Many variations of rotational shapes for the Qi washings of the penis and scrotum should be used.

When doing such exercises, you should also massage the flesh on top of the sacrum by rubbing it 36 times in a clockwise direction, and 36 times in a counter-clockwise direction. This also means you should mentally rotate the

Qi inside your sacrum 36 times in each direction as well. Two sets of nerves, six each, leave the sacrum from each of its sides, which is why the sacral or sex chakra is said to have six petals. In addition to this massage of the sacrum, you should also rotate your Qi in the belt of flesh above the scrotum that runs around the waist.

An excellent exercise is to breath into your sacrum (rather than *dantian*) upon inhalation and then lead that energy into the left side of your genitals to wash them, then out the left side of the penis and scrotum back to the tailbone after completion. With a subsequent breath you lead it into the sacrum and from there into the right side of your penis and scrotum, and then when withdrawing it you return it to the sacrum. You need to do this in alternate fashion many times per session. This is called "Purifying Samantabhadra's Six-tusked Elephant" and should become a standard part of yoga, martial arts and spiritual practice. You can even rotate that Qi "throughout the elephant's head" when it reaches the genitals.

The Chinese Taoist practice of *Wo* used in the martial arts entails inhaling Qi into your scrotum and testicles as well as performing various massages that will stretch all the groin tissues. This is equivalent to doing yoga *asanas* to stretch the muscles and ligaments for this region and thereby improving its Qi flow, which incidentally might help with virility issues.[11] There are techniques for both men and women, but I will only describe those for males.

Wo for men entails holding the scrotum in the hands while stretching and massaging its various structural components, basically in as many ways and directions as possible without causing damage. One technique is to cup the testicles with both hands, hold them up, and then use the thumbs to lightly press and massage them. You need to also roll the penis between the palms, and stretch any ligaments or tissues within the scrotum that are possible. This method includes massage routines for the penis and scrotum such as *long zhu zhang gong, long jin shen qi-gong, long jin zhan qi-gong, shou dao gong, shou*

---

[11] Taking nattokinase also dissolves blood clots in the tiny capillaries leading to the penis, which often become highly occluded due to cigarette smoking and diabetes, and thus usually helps some people with virility issues. Getting off high blood pressure medication is often a solution as well to virility issues such as erectile dysfunction.

pai gong and *zhuan zhu gong.*[12]

For instance, with *long jin ren gong*, or Dragon Tendon Strengthening, you would wrap your hand around the part of the genitals closest to the abdomen (their root) and then pull down to stretch the muscles and ligaments, switching hands so that each hand does this several dozen times. You would also pull the stretch to the left or the right as well as up and down. In some penis stretching exercises you would grab it at its base, pull it up and circle it from right to left 30-50 times, and then left to right 30-50 times, and then pull it forward and release it 30-50 times. Since this is not a book on specific stretching techniques, only the briefest indications are given for such methods. The primary purpose is to tell you of their importance for the highest martial arts attainments, and to inform you of their existence.

The second *Wo* method for men is a method Taoism calls "withdrawing the turtle" or "withdrawing the sword." With this method you sit on the edge of a chair so that your genitals hang loose. You then hold up the penis from underneath using a hand palm that faces downwards. Next you inhale, drawing in your abdomen while making the penis *tighter and tighter.* During the yoga exercise of *nauli kriya* you suck in your abdomen to pull it against your spine as tightly as possible, and with *mula bandha* you contract the pelvic muscles from various angles to compress them. However, with this method you work primarily on the penis. While inhaling, you pull in your penis as tightly as possible and simultaneously hold up your anus and perineum slightly since this helps in the retraction. When contracting you can at times try to pull your Qi away from your penis so that it feels a bit cold. You repeat this at least ten times with one hand and then repeat ten times with the other.

Celibacy, or *brahmacarya,* is sexual continence or abstinence that for a man essentially means semen retention. One of the purposes of abstaining from sex with a partner, and refraining from ejaculation through masturbation, is that the preservation of Jing and Qi (since they are not lost through ejaculation) means you are preserving power within your body. That

---

[12] See Yang Jwing-ming's *Qigong the Secret of Youth: Da Mo's Muscle/Tendon Changing and Marrow/Brain Washing Classics* and Mantak Chia's *Bone Marrow Nei Kung.*

accumulated power helps to open up the Qi channels within the genitals and pelvis, which is why men feel uncomfortable when that force accumulates and starts exerting itself to open up blocked Qi channels within those tissues. To learn many types of advanced martial arts skills it is therefore important that men practice celibacy for periods of time.

The *Surangama Sutra* of Buddhism says, "The difference between the worldly and the saintly … depends solely on the elimination or not of sexual desire." The explanation of this phrase is found within the Indian yoga text *Hatharatnavali* that advises, "Jing (semen) as well as mind should be preserved with effort." Hanuman was famous for his celibacy. As to Sun Wu-Kong, his teacher Subhuti instructed him:

> Know well this secret formula wondrous and true:
> Spare and nurse the vital forces, this and nothing else.
> All power resides in the semen, the breath, and the spirit (Jing, Qi and Shen);
> Guard these with care, securely, lest there be a leak.
> Lest there be a leak! Keep within the body!
> Hearken to my teaching and the Way itself will prosper.[13]

Sun Wu-Kong therefore kept his pole in his ear. The pole represented his Qi, and in some cases his (extendable) penis or virility. It was kept in his ear because there is a connection between the kidneys, ears, and your vitality. Furthermore, the power from below must travel up your spine to your head, so Sun Wu-Kong was said to store his pole in his ear to represent the power of virility from his kidneys. The highest yoga and martial arts attainments depend upon the principle of not losing too much Jing, Qi or Shen.

Men feel pressure internally when they don't ejaculate after many days, but that pressure indicates that their Qi is working on opening up the circulatory obstructions to Qi flow within the tissues of their pelvis and groin. Due to celibacy that energy is not lost, and due to accumulation it can then be used to open up internal Qi pathways for yoga attainments and

---

[13] *The Journey to the West*, trans. by Anthony Yu, (The University of Chicago Press, Chicago, 1978).

martial arts excellence.

If you work very hard at pelvic exercises that fully stretch its muscles and tendons, less sexual pressure will build up inside the hips and pelvis because the vital energy that normally resides within this region will finally become able to freely circulate everywhere else in the body to help open up energy channels elsewhere due to that extra flow. For instance, if you make it a habit to hold your energy in your *dantian* (lower abdomen) as taught in the martial arts, you will pull energy from elsewhere into this region and wash the tissues along the way.

An issue that often bothers martial artists who work hard is involuntary ejaculation through wet dreams at night. One remedy is to practice before every bedtime the "flying bird" form from yoga and Taoism where you pull the energy from the sacrum and pelvis into your head while rising on your toes and simultaneously raising your arms like wings. To practice the technique, stand straight like a tree. Inhaling slowly but deeply, rise on your toes and bring the arms from your side to touch above your head. As you perform the inhalation, pull the energy from your pelvis into your sacrum and then upwards through your spine into your head. While rising on your feet, look upwards at your hands that are being brought together to touch one another above your head. Upon exhalation, slowly come back down again to rest on your feet while simultaneously bringing your arms back down to your sides. You repeat this three to five times just before bedtime to prevent wet dreams and ejaculation.

There are many different techniques to cultivate the Qi within different parts of your body, and various methods to purify both the Yin and Yang nature of these areas. For specific results, specific methods are practiced. With this school of approaches, you work on cultivating the Qi of independent body segments and then you later combine the energy of all the pieces into one seamless whole.

This is exactly how Olympic athletes train because they are taught to master complicated movements by mastering smaller chunks that are later assembled together into one continuous larger sequence. After each chunk is mastered they link it with the others already perfected in a smooth unbroken series. In other words, they break movements down into basic components and have athletes learn each element separately. Only later do they try to link everything together into a flawless harmonious movement. Component learning is superior to trying to learn an entire sequence at once.

You must eventually link together the energy of the upper and lower body regions, and the Qi of all your appendages however minor or seemingly unimportant they are for martial arts, into one unity.

The end target is always the same. You want to improve the flow of Qi throughout your body everywhere, and especially the pathways involved with the movements essential for the martial arts. Eventually you want to create such good internal Qi circulation that your movements are graceful, flow like water, and you feel your entire body as one unit of energy because you have united the Qi of all body segments into one uninterrupted unity. You *are* basically energy with a certain form. You want to reach the stage through your martial arts training where your physical nature becomes just one body of energy without divisions. This is the basis of the highest state of "flow."

Men and women typically practice sitting meditation, where they rest in mental peace and stillness, with the same objective. They aim to give birth to Qi through the passivity of meditation practice where the state of mental Yin produces Yang Qi within the body. The idea is that it arises and then circulates everywhere inside themselves clearing out energy restrictions until the body becomes a single flowing unit. However, the movement practices within the martial arts are far faster for developing your Qi and unifying with the Tao.

Martial artists exercise all their muscles and then can practice leading their Qi through their muscles to produce a higher realm of attainment in a much quicker and complete fashion than what is normally achieved through just meditation alone. In martial arts training of just muscular/movement exercises alone you are already directly working to get rid of Qi flow impediments within your body rather than just waiting for this to happen, as is the case with meditation practice. When you add Qi exercises to the practice of forms then you have a more powerful combination for transformation.

An ideal training regime for children is to have them simultaneously learn yoga and *jiu jitsu, taijiquan* or Shaolin and Wudang *kung-fu* when young. Particularly useful are the following forms: *xiao hong quan, xuan gong quan, da bong quan, fu hu quan, wu bu quan* and *lian huan quan.*

As they get older and their minds become more developed, they can be taught meditation and begin to specialize in the soft martial arts of *taijiquan, xingyiquan, baguazhang, tongbeiquan, yiquan* or *liu he ba fa* that can lead to transcendental attainments because they entail mastering inner Qi flow. Naturally, any of the simple sequences of animal forms in the martial arts can be learned at a young age as well, or simple methods like *Yi Jin Jing,* since they do not require the mental maturity required for mastering inner Qi energies. A big benefit is that once learned when young, when older people can return to these exercises for purposes of health maintenance since they already leaned them.

Mastering your internal energy will cause tremendous changes within your body. These exercises, normally kept secret, offer you a new territory of training that will lead to the upper echelons of achievement.

8
BINDUS OR POINTS

The Chinese say that martial arts and Chinese traditional medicine come from the same roots. In fact, both of these schools share a relevant commonality in having identified a variety of sensitive spots and critical cavities on the human body that can be used in special ways.

These various sensitive points or spots, also known as *bindus*, are known as marma points in Ayurvedic medicine. In Chinese medicine they are known as the acupuncture points located along the Qi channels or meridians of inner Qi flow. Many are embryological organizing centers of the body that it uses to grow, and which remain sensitive after maturity. However, there are many other sensitive points and cavities not located on classical acupuncture lines.

For instance, in AMIT therapy the muscles of your body that are found to be weak or "shut off" because of prior damage, and whose loads have been transferred to adaptations (other muscles in order to lighten their loads), are restored to normal functioning by treating seven reflex points. These include a weakened muscle's origin and insertion points on the bone, neurovascular point, neurolymphatic point, spindle cell point, two organ or gland reflex points and its acupuncture point.

The various sensitive body points man has discovered over the centuries can be used for healing people, such as in the arts of massage or acupuncture, but also in the martial arts. You can heal patients by applying Qi (or pressure) to these points, or you can use the points as striking targets or to get rid of a grasp. You can also recite sounds upon these points in order to energize the Qi in their surrounding vicinity.

Many masters practice "poison touch" striking methods to inflict damage to opponents at special point locations because when force is applied to some *bindu* locations it can knock you unconscious. Force applied to others might paralyze you or even cause death.

The martial arts have many types of palms and striking methods for various target areas that include these points and other "blood gate" or nerve plexus targets. For instance, there are (more than) 36 *Dim mak* points throughout the body that can be used to kill or incapacitate opponents if shocking power is applied to them effectively. However, it is said that some of the masters of the soft martial arts, rather than those who have mastered Iron Shirt *gong-fu*, can absorb strikes to these points by transforming the hard shock to lightness.

Of the hundreds of possible acupuncture points, pressure points, sensitive cavities, and striking targets, the following should be of major interest because they are gates by which the Qi can pass in and out of the body due to your training:

- The *Yongquan* "Bubbling Well" cavity (acupuncture point K-1) at the bottom of feet can unite with the heavy rooted Qi of the Earth, so martial artists practice connecting with the Earth's Qi through this foot point to develop better grounding and surer footing. In Taoism "breathing" doesn't simply refer to the movement of air in and out of the lungs but to a process involving the whole body, and in true Taoism connected with the martial arts you don't "breath from your heels" as Zhuangzi said, but from this point.
- The *Laogong* "Labor Palace" cavity (acupuncture point P-8) in the palm of both hands is excellent for issuing Qi from the body for explosive strikes that can even split stone, and for drawing Qi into the body to feed the network of Qi channels within it.

- The *Baihui* "Hundred Meetings" cavity on the top of the head (acupuncture point DU-20 on the *du mai*) is used to draw Qi into the body from Heaven. It is on the crown of the head where all the ascending Qi of the body converges, and is located right above the Mud ball (Pellet) Palace, or brainstem.

Through special exercises you can learn to breath Qi into or out of these cavities, which is practiced in many of the soft martial arts schools. Typically most exercises have you inhale your breath and lead your Qi deep inside your body to your organs, bones and marrow or *dantian*, and with exhalation you lead Qi through your limbs to these five centers (head, two *Laogong* points in the palms and two *Yongquan* points in the soles of the feet).

Yogi masters recite *bijas,* which are the root syllable sounds of mantras, on the body's acupuncture points in order to stir up the Qi within their vicinity and activate the acupuncture meridian (fascial plane) upon which they lay. This is also a practice in Taoism and Esoteric Buddhism, as well as a secret practice within the higher martial arts, and was practiced by the female tantric adept Yeshe Tsogyel. It is a means of cultivating the Qi in a particular vicinity by placing sound energy upon the points.

Different sounds are used for different body locations because they vibrationally resonate the area more effectively. Examples of sounds that vary according to location are found in the *Mahavairocana Sutra* and *Yoga Yajnavalkya*.

One example of using *bindus* (points) is the *Song Jing Jianshen Gong* method of Taoism. In this method, rather than pronouncing sounds upon selected body points you progressively relax your body by mentally relaxing *bindus* in a progressive series, namely specific acupuncture points. You can do this while sitting, standing, or lying down, but you start from points in the head and work downwards to your feet.

The sequence proceeds as follows: you mentally bring your mind to a *bindu* and then relax that region starting at the *baihui* (on top of the head) and moving to the *yintang* (on the forehead), next to both *jianjing* (on top of the shoulders), to *shanzhong* (midpoint of the nipples on the chest), to the *dantian* (four fingers below the navel), *huiyin* (on the perineum), to *yinlingquan*, to *sanyinjiao*, to *yongquan*, and then to your big toe, second toe, third toe, fourth toe and finally your small toe on both feet.

A related method of energizing your body, starting from your head, recites sounds upon and within *bindus*, locations, organs and appendages. Starting from the head you recite "Om" (within the entire head but especially feeling the *baihu* point at its crown), "Ah" at the *yintang* third eye region on the forehead and behind it filling the nasal cavity with sound, "Chr" for the teeth and gums, "Jha" in the tongue, at the back of the mouth, along the throat and in the thyroid region; and "Rah" at the *shanzhong* point and in the middle of the chest.

Next, "Pha" in the region of the chest and back, followed by "Bha" in the shoulder bones and at the *jianjing* GB21 acupuncture point on top of the shoulders, "Hreem" along the entire insides of the upper arm, "Shreem" similarly within the entire meat of the lower arm containing the radius and ulna bones (and centered around the TW8 and LU8 acupuncture points), and "Tah" at the *laogong* "Labor Palace" cavity (acupuncture point P-8) in the palm of both hands.

Continuing, "Hoo" in the stomach region, followed by "Ssss" in the two lungs, "Foo" within the two kidneys, "Shoo" within the liver, and "Vam" for the lower abdomen, which is the lowermost torso of your body.

Lastly, "Lam" for the *dantian*, "Tah" for your perineum to within your private parts (you are supposed to feel the Qi within your genitals), "Bam" within the upper leg (the muscles surrounding and including the femur bone), "Dam" within the lower leg (centered on the *chengshan* BL57 acupuncture point) and "Tam" within the feet or at the *Yongquan* "Bubbling Well" cavity (acupuncture point K-1) at the bottom of both feet.

This is like a mantra:

> Om Ah Chr Jha Rah
> Pha Bha Hreem Shreem Tah

Hoo Ssss Foo Shoo Vam
Lam Tah Bam Dam Tam.

You can think of it this way:

Om (head) Ah (nasal cavity and forehead) Chr (teeth and gums) Jha (throat
and thyroid) Rah (heart and chest)
Pha (chest and back) Bha (shoulder bones and shoulders) Hreem (upper
arms) Shreem (lower arms) Tah (hands)
Hoo (stomach) Ssss (lungs) Foo (kidneys) Shoo (liver) Vam (lower
abdomen with *dantian*)
Lam (*dantian*) Tah (private parts) Bam (thighs) Dam (lower legs) Tam (feet).

A similarly constructed mantra, composed of individual mantras that
stimulate (and thus open) the Qi channels within different sections of your
body defined through different partitionings, is as follows:

Rah Vah
Om Ah Hung
Om Ah Vah Lah
Hoo Sss Foo Shoo Vam
Hung

You can recite it in this manner:

Rah (right side of body) Vah (left side of body)
Om (head and arms) Ah (chest and arms) Hung (lower torso and legs)
Om (head) Ah (chest with middle *dantian*, and arms) Vah (middle torso)
Lah (lower torso with *dantian*, and legs)
Hoo (stomach) Sss (lungs) Foo (kidneys) Shoo (liver) Vam (*dantian*)
Hung (lower abdomen with *dantian*, legs and feet)

You can construct many mantras efficient at vibrating your Qi if you use
sounds that especially affect body sections, organs, limbs, meridians, or
points and then direct the sounds at or within those sections during
recitation. This is a matter of innovation for what works. As an example,
you might add an "Om" or "Ram" at the front of this mantra to vibrate all

the Qi of your body if it helps.

Many hymns in Christianity are sung in such a way that the sounds come from different parts of the body, thus resonating their Qi and thereby illustrating this principle. They are specifically designed for this purpose, which is to move, stimulate or excite the Qi in different parts of the body in a sequential fashion. Many variations of this practice are possible. For instance, when reciting "Ah" you might feel the energy start in your head and move towards your feet as you hold the syllable, or start from your feet and move upwards, or start within your stomach area and move outwards everywhere, and so on for each syllable respectively. Once you find a sound that vibrates the QI of the body or body section, you can recite it in many ways.

THE THREE *DANTIAN*

Larger than a small *bindu* point are the three *dantian* of the body that can be used to project energy into other areas of the body or into space. These are the upper *dantian*, middle *dantian*, and lower *dantian*. Each *dantian* contains a central point of focus that can be used as a target for concentration or Qi vibration. In other words, at the center of all these regions is a point that can serve as a center of concentration practice.

For the upper *dantian*, or head, that center is the middle of the brain or the bulbous top of the brainstem. The brainstem is known the "pedestal" in Buddhism and as the "mud pellet" or "mud pill palace" in the Taoist martial arts. This is actually the true *Ajna* chakra of yoga. When the Buddhist sutras state that a Buddha projected light rays from between his eyebrows it refers to the workings of the brainstem rather than the pineal gland, pituitary gland or "third eye" point just above the nose between the eyebrows. The ray of light refers to active working consciousness, and the activities of consciousness occur within the brainstem.

To open up the upper *dantian*, which once opened will not only bring clarity to your thinking but also improve your martial arts reaction times, the most efficient practice is to obtain DTI (diffusion tensor imaging) pictures of the cranial nerves, and to wash the brain with mind-led Qi rotations that caress the nerve pathways via the patterns revealed in the pictures. When you visualize energy running through your muscles, such as when maintaining a yoga posture or martial arts pose, you should also use pictures of the activated muscles to guide your efforts.

In yoga the brain is the *Sahasrara* chakra, and all its petals are actually the brain's neurons and nerves. Once they are opened it is easier to enter into calm mental states since the circulatory pathways of Qi within the brain will then have been cleansed of obstructions. What is particularly difficult to open is the cerebellum. If the energy flows more efficiently throughout the brain then your mental state will be more peaceful. Now, since the brainstem or *Ajna* chakra has two sections, Yin and Yang or left and right, you can practice alternately "breathing into" each section to help open them, or wash them using other different *neijia* methods.

The middle *dantian* is often called the "crimson palace." It is the region of the middle of the chest at the level of the heart, which is the *Anahata* chakra area of yoga. The middle *dantian* is anchored into the heart center. This center, and sometimes the actual heart organ itself, are both used as a focus point of concentration in some cultivation methods. Because of this focus, many practitioners forget that it is actually the Qi channels of the tissues within the entire chest region that need to be opened, including the washing of the lungs and rib bones. Thus, any Qi methods that concentrate on this region should progressively work at transforming the entire Qi of the chest containing heart, lungs, ribs, thymus gland, spine and skin.

While the thinking (consciousness) activities of the brainstem are symbolized by light rays projecting from the forehead, the feelings of joy and happiness, compassion and loving-kindness, friendliness and goodwill, generosity and giving are usually symbolized as being projected from the heart either through the arms or in a way that forms a great sphere around the body. Also centered around the middle of the chest, this sphere radiates infinitely outward into space in all directions. A popular cultivation technique for purifying your Qi and transforming your attitudes is to hold onto one of these emotions and imagine it radiating infinitely outwards around you.

Alternatively, in martial arts training you can try to feel the heart Qi meridian that runs down the arm into the palms of the hands (and then make it run to *all the fingers instead of just the middle digit*) whenever you engage in acts of giving, generosity, feel tremendously expressive with joy and so on. In other words, whenever you feel joy or generosity, the positive feelings can be projected from your heart center and through the arms during expression. You can do this with all the positive emotions of your internal organs to help open up meridians and strengthen the organs, especially when you practice holding immeasurably large emotions to do so.

The lower *dantian,* where the body's center of gravity is located, is the main area of concentration in many martial arts. This is because most torso muscles and many body movements proceed from that area, and because energy from below to above must also pass through this region. When we were in the womb we received nutrition from our mother directly into the lower *dantian* so it is an extremely important area for internal Qi flow. Because most of our alimentary canal (the long tube of our gut starting from the esophagus to the anus) is located within the *dantian* and since our intestines contain more neurons than found in the spine, this gut brain of ours that influences our moods and emotions is often called the lower brain of the body.

The brain in the head and in the gut are connected through the spinal cord, which is a pathway of Qi communication between these two poles. Because of this fact, when opening the microcosmic circulation an alternative method of mind-guided rotation is to grab the Qi of the entire lower gut and intestines and then bring that total Qi up the spine into the brain, and then descend it back down to the lower abdomen through the front *and middle of the body*.

Also known as the "golden stove," the *dantian* is considered of premier importance in *qi-gong, nei-gong* and the martial arts. It is often a focus point for meditation because students are taught to center their mind within their body at the *dantian,* which is several centimeters below the navel within the center of the lower abdomen. Its exact location slightly differs from person to person, and many martial arts schools will teach a different method to locate it, but as a general rule it exists behind the _Qihai_ acupuncture point.

One particular practice is to rotate the Qi within your lower _dantian_ by setting up a forward and then downward rotation of the energy within this region. It takes a while to become able to fully turn the energy within the lower _dantian_. You have to first contact and feel the internal energy of the area, and then rotate it forwards and downwards as if you were turning a ball. In that rotation it will be turning up from your backside when the front of the energy ball is rotated forward and descends. Sometimes individuals will experience diarrhea or vomiting when they commence upon this practice, but this purification stage quickly passes.

This practice is actually an alternative to the Qi purification exercise of guiding your Qi along the shape of your intestines. Because you cannot guide your Qi along the twisting, irregular shape of your intestines that cannot be predicted, during sitting postures you can rotate the Qi within your _dantian_ as taught, or simply circulate your Qi in your lower abdomen and pelvis by moving it everywhere with washing rotations of every possible direction.

In martial arts you have to find the center of the _dantian_ because all power and movement passes through this region. It is a primary spot in the martial arts because most Qi in martial arts movements is transmitted through the _dantian_ via the energy channel systems into the rest of the body, and certainly for striking motions. It isn't just a critical transmission area for physical forces that must traverse the body from below to above. Therefore, martial arts practitioners are taught to build up Qi in their lower _dantian_ region and then lead it to the skin or limbs along the pathway of muscles or lines of the acupuncture meridians.

If you build up a lot of energy within the _dantian_, it will start to radiate out of your body into the space around you. You can feel the energy radiating from very advanced martial artist masters and from many yoga spiritual masters, who will sometimes manipulate it in order to affect the Qi within their environment. If you are near such individuals when they are doing this you will often feel their power through a pressure on or within your body, and for some individuals it can even raise the hair on their skin. This Qi is naturally impregnated with one's personality, but with practice you can consciously give it a Qi-tone or characteristic of your own choosing, and radiate that feeling in a larger sphere around your body or project it into the environment.

This principle is taught in the stories of the Kuan Yin, the Bodhisattva of compassion, who descends into the Avici hells of fire that immediately become cooled and pacified through his presence. All the beings within the hells are thereby relieved of their suffering because of his appearance, which is radiating compassion and other good qualities everywhere. The King of Hell, Yama, wonders why this has happened and then praises Kuan Yin for his cultivation of virtue when he finds out that these events were caused simply through his presence.

While the Taoist martial arts teach that such radiance comes primarily from the *dantian*, the heart field can similarly radiate the Qi of the emotions into the environment through its own field effects. This is one of the purposes behind Buddhist immeasurable meditations. Properly speaking, it is only when the body becomes a single unit of energy that this power is fully manifested, and then it radiates from the entire body rather than from the upper, middle or lower *dantian*. However, you can learn to project your Qi from your three separate *dantian* through training, and should practice this. At that level it exhibits the temperament of an individual's personality unless tuned for a different purpose to influence the environment or others.

SPECIAL TIMES

Another segment of interest is that of time rather than the body. According to Chinese Taoism, the day is divided into twelve two-hour blocks that mark the passage of time as well as the growth and decay of the Yin Qi and Yang Qi of the Earth. From midnight the Yang Qi of the Earth grows slowly until dawn. The morning contains the strongest Yang Qi of the day whereas the evening contains the strongest Yin Qi of the day.

Four of these time periods are of special interest to the martial arts community because they represent crucial timings for Yin Qi and Yang Qi cultivation. They are the "four doors" for Yin and Yang's entrance and exit in the world because this is when Yin and Yang change in nature. Martial artists can learn to absorb Qi at these four timings to help their practice:

- Yang Qi is initiated between 11 pm – 1 am, which is the Chinese hour of *Zi*; this is a time to cultivate one's spirit (that is overly Yin in nature)
- Yang Qi emerges at 5 am – 7 am, which is the Chinese hour of *Mao*; it is a period of strong Yang Qi that can be taken advantage of for particular *gong-fu* practices
- Yin Qi is initiated at 11 am – 1 pm, which is the Chinese hour of *Wu*; this is a time to inhale Yin Qi and nourish one's blood (that is overly Yang in nature)
- Yin Qi grows stronger between 5 pm – 7 pm, which is the Chinese hour of *You*; it is a period of strong Yin Qi that you can take advantage of for particular *gong-fu* practices

As an example, if you feel it is necessary to harmonize excessive Yin Qi within your body you can absorb Yang Qi from the sun to do so at an appropriate hour. You can stand or sit with your back to the sun where the Yang energy can be easily absorbed into your spine and then combine with the Yin Qi within your spinal fluid. The two essences will then mix and travel up the *du mai* channel of the spine that ascends over the head and then drops down in the front of your body. Alternatively, you can just try to absorb it into your entire body.

A cornerstone of *neijia* yoga is to understand practices like this, and the fact that there is no predetermined amount of time for absorbing Yin or Yang energy. You have to develop a feeling for when you're done. Hence in *neijia* (*nei-gong*) you need to become able to sense the Qi of Heaven and Earth and know the special times for practice to draw those energies into your body to replenish it.

9

LEADING YOUR QI THROUGH CIRCUITS (*PRATYAHARA*)

You can concentrate your Qi at special points (*bindus*) on your body in order to stimulate those points and bring more Qi into their vicinity. This will bath the region around the *bindu* in more Qi by drawing your Qi through meridians to that point, and thus this will also help improve the Qi flow along those circulatory pathways. In other words, you concentrate on a *bindu* in order to stimulate meridians *and* regions.

You can also practice directly leading or guiding your Qi along the meridians within your body. Further, you can concentrate your Qi within certain selected areas of your body, or energize your Qi within those sections, and you can also rotate your Qi within those regions through various mind-led Qi revolutions. This includes Qi work that bathes your limbs and appendages to purify their Qi and meridians. You can also lead your Qi from one section to another within your body, like a traveler on a pilgrimage, until you "wash" your entire inner body. These are all the internal yoga practices that constitute the true purpose of yoga in terms of purifying *nadis*, but which are not discussed within simplistic texts like the *Hatha Yoga Pradipika* or Patanjali's *Yoga Sutras*.

To reach the highest levels of martial arts you need to learn how to use your mind to lead your Qi efficiently. You need to learn how to control the flow of Qi through your body using your intent, and to make certain Qi flows more natural and efficient. You must train your inner Qi body just as much as your physical body. Qi is the root and foundation of physical strength so you must build up your capabilities for being able to manipulate this fundamental root.

The Chinese discovered centuries ago that vital energy flows to all parts of the through pathways it calls "meridians." Like rivers that branch into tributaries and then endless smaller streams, a similar network of energy distribution flows throughout your body every moment. Acupuncture and acupressure are methods for regulating and balancing the distribution of this energy throughout the body by manipulating key points along this distribution network of meridians. If this vital flow of energy is interrupted at one or more locations, health problems will result that might cause pain, unconsciousness or even death, which is the basis of the mart arts method of striking *Dim mak* points on the body. Through strikes, aggressors attempt to interrupt the Qi flow at vital *Dim mak* locations on opponents that will then incapacitate them. In *Kyusho Jitsu*, or pressure point fighting, practitioners are taught to apply pressure or strike at pressure points on the body to cause pain.

The smooth circulation of Qi energy throughout your body without stagnation, interruption, blockage or obstruction is the basis of good health. One of the objectives of martial arts is to produce a state of great health where this energy is able to flow unhindered throughout all these pathways so that a practitioner attains a peaceful mind, develops sharpened senses, and is in harmony with themselves and their environment. The martial arts should also help to circulate your Qi to improve your health and heal your body, and also increase your longevity.[14]

In martial arts, you need to train your mind to lead your Qi to the muscles to energize them so that they function more efficiently. The outside and the inside, the muscles and their Qi, must combine. From posture to posture, you want the internal power to be unbroken. If you train your concentration and use your mind properly you can lead your Qi to energize your muscles to a level that manifests power to its maximum, and which will increase fighting effectiveness.

Qi-gong and then *nei-gong* are necessary for reaching these higher levels of

---

[14] See *Look Younger, Live Longer* by William Bodri.

fighting ability. Their training involves developing Qi, eliminating obstructions to its internal circulation within you, and then matching the motion of your internal Qi with the movement of the external form.

Training for the external or "hard" martial arts works on developing your muscles and aerobic abilities. It energizes the muscles in the limbs with Qi so that they can manifest maximum strength. On the other hand, the "soft" or internal styles of martial arts believe that you need to learn how to circulate and build up Qi in order for your physical body to manifest its maximum power. There is thus an emphasis on softness in the muscles so that Qi can flow most efficiently.

Training in the "soft" martial arts therefore focuses on circulating and building up Qi internally. Every movement must involve mental intent, Yi, and your Qi. To do this the body must to some degree remain relaxed and soft since this maximizes the flowingness of internal Qi circulation.

The mechanics of internal practices rely on fairly specific alignments, but the major principle other than correct positioning is that you need to get rid of unnecessary tension within your body and practice softness for your Qi to flow better. Your mind should also be calm so that you do not disturb the Qi from assuming its most natural and powerful flowing pattern. With the proper body positioning and alignment the Qi will start flowing automatically, which should be matched by a mental state of inner tranquility. All the body's parts should feel comfortable, light and agile and become smoothly threaded together for the Qi to flow without needing force. In this way the Qi everywhere will be naturally connected without obstructions.

The soft martial arts use *wai-dan* and *nei-dan* exercises to free the body's Qi circulatory routes of obstructions, build up Qi in the body and then lead it out to the limbs. They focus on learning how to build up the Qi, circulate it, and apply it in the physical body. You want to make the Qi circulate smoothly and strongly in your body. You want to learn how to accumulate or build up your Qi to a high level to strengthen your body. Third, you want to become able to lead your Qi to your skin, organs, bones, and muscles upon call, and the training for this includes various internal routines for washing your entire body with Qi.

These objectives require progressive training to control your Qi and lead it everywhere inside your body, as well as to match it with your movements.

To wash your internal body with Qi in order to reduce bottlenecks and obstructions within its circulatory routes, such as meridians or connected muscle pathways, you should learn how to lead your Qi with your mind. You must learn how to stimulate your Qi with your breathing or physical movements or emotions. You must learn how to recite mantras or *bija* sounds on body regions, on *bindu* points, or upon Qi pathways that need to be freed of obstructions so that Qi circulation within that pathway improves. You need to know how to apply visualizations to those areas while arousing emotions to activate your Yin Qi or Yang Qi in those areas and hence free the Qi flow of hindrances and interruptions.

All body regions must be washed with *both* Yin Qi and Yang Qi, and not just Yang Qi alone. This is a secret few understand. Since individuals naturally concentrate on developing Yang Qi, their Yin Qi accumulation and purification is insufficient, and knowing masters undertake seemingly unusual practices to cultivate their Yin essence.

Here then is the *neijia* yoga basic sequence of practice. After first learning how to concentrate Qi within a region; stimulate it using emotions, sound power or visualizations; and wash it through mentally guided circulations; next using your will you should draw your Qi from one point to another, which is possible because your Qi will follow your thought. You should temporarily hold it at various vital spots and swirl it hundreds of times at those locations during each practice session just as you would practice a martial arts form countless times. Then you can move it to another section in a special sequence until you have activated the Qi in your entire body.

At any location you should rotate your Qi clockwise followed by counterclockwise, counterclockwise followed by clockwise, and swirl it up and down in revolutions, or to the left and right, always changing the order. Swirl it countless times, and add purifying toning emotions of Yin or Yang to your set. This is the way to do it, the secret recipe for transformation.

The practice of leading your Qi from place to place within your body, and rotating it at those spots, is a yoga practice called *pratyahara*. Instead of focusing on your external senses, you withdraw that focus to concentrate on manipulating the Qi inside your body at a sequence of spots.

This is essentially *anapana, nei-gong, nei-dan*, inner energy (Qi) work, *kriya yoga, kundalini yoga*, tantric yoga, or Vajrayana practice. Make no mistake about it, this is the esoteric school of spiritual development.

PATHWAYS AND CONTAINERS

The *Nitya-natha-paddhati* teaches "sixteen containers" where you can lead and concentrate your Qi: your big toes, anus, rectum and sphincter, male genital organs (scrotum and penis), entrails in the lower abdomen, navel area, heart, throat, uvula, naso-pharynx, root of the tongue, base of the upper teeth, tip of the nose, base of the nose, point between the eyebrows, and eyes. You can practice leading your Qi to these or other locations and holding it at these vital points. Then you have the option of washing those locations, or not, with many Qi rotations because sometimes you need to hold your Qi at locations.

The *Hathatatvakaumudi* teaches to hold your Qi at the feet, toes, heels, ankles, thighs, knees, anus, genitals, navel, heart, throat, lips, tongue, nose, eyes, and head with full concentration. You must also swirl it around and feel it inside these regions.

Yogi Boganathar teaches that you should lead your Qi from the big toes to the ankle, knee, thigh, genitals, navel, heart, neck, uvula, nose, space between the eyebrows, forehead and then crown of the head.

The sage Yajnavalkya teaches that you should lead your Qi from the big toes to the following vital points: the ankles, then into the mid-shanks, the root of the calves, the knees, middle of the thighs, root of the anus (perineum), the center of the body (*dehamadhya*), generative organ, the navel, the heart, and neck pit, the root of the palate, the root of the nose, circular orb of the eyes, the center of the eyebrows, the forehead, and then crown of the head. The *Mahavairocana Sutra* offers *bija* mantra sounds for several of these locations.

Yogi Yajnavalkya also teaches, "Some skilled yogis speak of [another] *pratyahara*. … During the practice of pranayama, the Prana (Qi) must be held by the mind from the big toe to the crown of the head, like a totally filled pot. Drawing [the Prana] from the crown of the head, one must focus it in the forehead. Again, drawing the Prana from the forehead, one must focus it between the eyebrows. Drawing [the Prana] from the center of the eyebrows one must focus it in the center of the eyes. Drawing the Prana from the eyes, one must focus it in the root of the nose. From the root of the nose, one must focus the Prana in the root of the tongue. Drawing [the Prana] from the root of the tongue, one must focus it in the base of the throat (neck-pit). Drawing the Prana from the neck-pit, one must focus it in the center of the heart, from the center of the heart one must focus it in the center of the navel, again from the center of the navel one must focus it in the generative organ and then from the generative organ one must focus it in the abode of fire (*dehamadhya*), from the *dehamadhya* (lower abdomen or *dantian* in the center of the body), one must focus it in the root of the anus and from the root of the anus in the [mid-] thighs, then from the mid-thigh in the center of the knees. Then, [from the knee] one must focus the Prana in the root of the calf, from there in the middle of the shank, and drawing [the Prana] from the middle of the shank in the ankle. From the ankle, one must focus it (the Prana) in the big toes of the feet."[15]

NYASA YOGA

The systemic rotation of your Qi at locations and guiding it to different body parts is called Nyasa Yoga.[16] Traditionally each set of Nyasa locations were supposed to be washed by the "powers of a deity" after you touched that location with reverence, but the actual purpose of the practice was for you to stimulate your Qi at each location as a type of Qi work that would

---

[15] *Yoga Yajnavalkya*, trans. by A.G. Mohan with Ganesh Mohan, (Svastha Yoga Pte Ltd, 2013), pp. 75-79.
[16] See *Nyasa Yoga*, by William Bodri.

naturally wash the tissues to free them of inhibiting obstructions over time.

The Ganesh Nyasa starts with concentrating your Qi in your head. After grabbing it and spinning it around you move to the Qi in your forehead, then right eye, left eye, right ear, left ear, right nostril, left nostril, right cheek, left cheek, upper lip, lower lip, upper teeth, lower teeth, tongue, throat, right shoulder, right elbow, right wrist, base of right fingers, right finger tips, left shoulder, left elbow, left wrist, left root of fingers, left finger tips, right thigh, right knee, right ankle, right foot, right toes, left thigh, left knee, left ankle, left foot, left toes, right side of the body, left side of the body, back, navel, belly, heart, right collar bone, shoulder hump, left collar bone, heart to right palm, heart to left palm, heart to right foot, heart to left foot, heart to genitals, and finally to your heart once again.

The Matrika Nyasa appends the sounds of the letters of the Sanskrit alphabet as *bija*-mantras to different body parts, and is therefore called the Garland of Letters. To practice this Nyasa you start by concentrating your Qi at your forehead and then sequentially move it to mouth, right eye, left eye, right ear, left ear, right nostril, left nostril, right cheek, left cheek, upper lip, lower lip, upper row of teeth, lower row of teeth, crown of the head, tip of the tongue, right shoulder and shoulder joint near armpit, right elbow, right wrist, base of the right hand fingers, fingertips of the right hand, left shoulder and shoulder joint near armpit, left elbow, left wrist, base of the left hand fingers, tips of the fingers of the left hand, right hip, right knee, right ankle, base of the toes of the right foot, tips of the toes of the right foot, left hip, left knee, left ankle, base of the fingers of the left foot, tips of the toes of the left foot, right side of the body, left side of the body, lower back, navel, stomach, heart, space on right shoulder between the right arm and neck, back of the head, space on left shoulder between the left arm and neck, move the Qi from the heart to the fingertips of the right hand, move the Qi from the heart to the fingertips of the left hand, move the Qi along the pathway from the whole right side and heart to the tips of the toes of the right foot, move the Qi along the pathway from the whole left side and heart to the tips of the toes of the left foot, abdomen, head.

The Nakshatra Nyasa, which pairs the Qi energy of body parts with the Nakshatra constellations (whose equivalents are the Chinese lunar mansions), recommends that you sequentially guide your Qi from your forehead to your right eye, left eye, right ear, left ear, right nostril, left nostril, throat, right shoulder, left shoulder, back, right elbow, left elbow, right wrist, left wrist, right hand, left hand, navel, pelvis, right thigh, left thigh, right knee, left knee, right ankle, left ankle, right foot, and left foot.

The Rasi Nyasa, which establishes correspondences with the twelve signs of the zodiac, is of interest because it is short, and cultivates the two sides of the penis. The genitals are an area particularly requiring Qi purification work that few martial arts or yoga exercises concentrate upon. The Rasi Nyasa starts from a foot on one side of your body and works upwards, as does the white skeleton visualization method, and then returns to the foot on the other side of your body after reaching your head and turning down. Starting with your right foot your guide your Qi upwards to the right side of the penis, right side of the belly and abdomen, right side of the heart and chest, right shoulder, right side of the head, left side of the head, left shoulder, left side of heart and chest, left side of the belly and abdomen, left side of penis, and left foot.

The Kara Nyasa, or Nyasa of the Hands, only works on opening up the Qi channels in the hands and fingers. It instructs you to lead the Qi to your thumbs, then forefinger, middle finger, ring finger, little finger, and then the front and back of the hands.

There are many ways to cultivate the Qi of the hands and fingers so that they do not become bottlenecks that hold up the entire circulation of Qi flow within the rest of the body due to poor circulation within these extremities.

In yoga, Esoteric Buddhism, Taoism, *Shugendo* and Shintoism, you practice various hand mudras in order to cultivate better Qi flow through each finger, such as in the practice of *Kuji-in* (Nine Hand Seals). While holding the mudras that have unusual finger positions, you are supposed to move your Qi through each of your fingers to their tips.

In Taoism you practice pulling Qi into the segments between the finger bones and pulling it upwards into the bones and outwards through the tip of the bones, doing all bone segments in series. Then you practice pulling Qi into the fingertips and segments between bones working towards the palms in order to pull it into the body. In this way you cultivate both ends of the bones.

In Tibetan Buddhism you are taught to lead the Qi to each finger in sequence while simultaneously visualizing (imagining) that each finger turns a different color: the thumbs become red when you push Qi through them, the forefinger becomes blue, the middle finger becomes yellow, the ring finger becomes green and the little finger becomes white.

For *taijiquan,* while in the *zhan zhang* standing pose you practice pulling Qi into the fingers to open their channels when practicing the method of "holding the ball." Lion Shape *baguazhang* practitioners also roll wooden balls (*qiu fa*) in order to develop Qi in the fingertips.

Toes are more difficult to cultivate. You can imagine your toes burning with fire or that they are burning candlesticks. This will not just pull your Qi energy to your feet but lower high blood pressure as a consequence.

Taoists focus on pulling Qi into the segments between each toe bone, as well as into the body through the *Yongquan* Bubbling Well K-1 acupuncture point located at the well of the foot. Martial artists are also taught to sink their Qi downwards to their feet or the K-1 point, just as they are taught to guide their Qi to the *Laogong* P-8 spot in the center of their palm. This has the purpose of focusing Qi on the center of the foot but does little for the Qi flow to your individual toes unless you make the effort to also send Qi to them individually, *as you should.*

The "soft" martial artists practice feeling that their feet become heavy either just through the first inch upwards through the sole, or throughout the foot entirely, in order to cultivate the feet and toes. In feeling that their feet become heavy and are rooted to the ground they are filling them with Yin Qi, which will often feel cold. *Baguazhang* also has the practice of "walking in the mud" (mud walking) that really sends Qi to the soles of your feet and thereby opens up the foot meridians, especially when combined with visualization that leads your Qi to your feet.

Incidentally, toe cultivation instructions were left to us in Buddhism and yoga by encoding them in Naga legends. Some Naga legends pertinent to the physical body say that serpent Naga beings, who have bodies of Qi, have five-sectioned hoods over their heads and live in the feet of cultivators. They are said to carry shining jewels in their foreheads that give them the light they need to be able to live in this dark realm of Yin Qi where Yang Qi has a hard time entering. Their hood refers to the webbing of ligaments in the feet that run to the toes, and their shining forehead jewel symbolizes the cultivation method of imagining that each toe bone shines with a bright white light, which will then bring Qi to the toes.

Of course, in other Naga legends the Nagas simply represent devas who have cultivated the five types of Qi within their body. This is more correct. They are represented as either having cobra-like hoods with five dragons on its segments (to represent having cultivated the Qi of the five elements of the body), or seven-dragon hoods (to represent having cultivated the Qi of the seven chakra segments of the body). When a great Naga therefore shelters Buddha with his hood, it represents a deva who has attained enlightenment by cultivating his or her Qi, and who comes to honor and protect the Buddha.

Yet in other legends a Naga is simply a coarse serpent (sometimes translated as a dragon) that is eaten by garudas (who symbolize the brain). The Naga represents the fact that your pelvic sexual energies travel up your spine like a snake, and then become purified by reaching your brain. Garuda (whose two wings represent the two brain lobes, whose feathers represent neurons, and whose head represents the brain stem) is fed by these ascending energies because he is the brain. The energies start in your pelvis and climb the *du mai* circulation upwards through your spine.

MERIDIAN PATHWAYS

From these examples you can see that there are all sorts of methods for cultivating the Qi within various body appendages so that they are no longer bottlenecks to inner Qi flow. Unfortunately, yogis and martial artists are rarely introduced to any at all. Postures and *asanas* are important, but so are methods for cultivating the Qi of each body section and appendage and eliminating interruptions to smoother Qi flow within them. To do this, stretching is not enough.

There are countless postures with endless variations but they are essentially nothing but configurations of Qi, and that Qi is one. Therefore you have to cultivate all the Qi of your body, within its separate parts, so that the divided can achieve unification in becoming one undivided Qi body. In fact, you must cultivate your muscles and their energy until your reach the deepest underlying foundational energy matrix of the human body. This corresponds to the highest stage of a yogi, Arhat or Taoist Immortal.

In martial arts the incorrect shape of the fingers comes from the correctness (proper placement) of the toes, just as the correct shape and movement of the arms comes from the legs. If the legs are tight then the arms will be tight and if the feet are clumsy the hands will be clumsy. Hence you can see the importance of learning proper placements, movements and cultivation of inner Qi flow within all these appendages that might seem unconnected with what you are doing elsewhere. You have to learn the proper body alignments, body movements, hand techniques, leg techniques and stepping strategies as well as proper breathing methods and Qi flow for all of these basics.

The simplest practice for leading your Qi from one section to another in your body is to work on clearing out obstructions within the microcosmic circulation that carries nerve impulses up your spine. This involves the *du mai* Qi channel within your spine and the *ren mai* channel that descends down the front of your body. Some individuals visualize the *ren mai* circulation as progressing downwards through our digestive organs or the endocrine glands since they are another cellular communication system that operates parallel to our nervous system. Although you can use breathing exercises to open this large circulatory orbit, most practitioners simply use their mind to lead their Qi in one great orbit hundreds of times per day to open these two meridians, which is called "making revolutions."

In the martial arts, it is the correct shape of the forms that is used to open up the acupuncture meridians of the body rather than having to push Qi through the meridians. Each posture in *taijiquan,* for instance, enhances Qi circulation in a special way, and each posture is to be practiced in a smooth, flowing manner, with its own special breathing pattern, in order to enliven the Qi in its natural circulatory paths. *Baguazhang* has postures that are designed to stimulate meridian Qi flow too.

In *baguazhang,* the Downward Sinking Palm (Xia Chen Zhang) posture opens, stimulates and strengthens the *ren mai* (Conception vessel), *du mai* (Governing vessel of the spine*)* and *chong mai* (Thrusting vessel) channels of the body. The Moon Embracing Palm posture (*Xia Chen Zhang*) opens and stimulates the Hand and Foot *Taiyin* meridian (Lung and spleen meridians) as well as Hand and Foot *Jueyin* (Pericardium and liver meridians). The Heaven Upholding Palm posture (*Tuo Tuan Zhang*) opens, stimulates and strengthens the Hand *Yangming* (Large intestine meridian) and Foot *Yangming* meridian (Stomach meridian). The Ball Rolling Palm posture (*Gui Qui Zhang*) will stimulate and help to open the Hand *Jueyin* (Pericardium meridian) and the Hand *Shaoyang* (Triple heater meridian). The Spear Upholding Palm posture (*Qiang Tuo Zhang*) helps to stimulate and open the Hand and Foot *Taiyang* (Small intestine and bladder meridians) and Hand and Foot *Shaoyin* (Heart and kidney meridians). The Heaven Pointing Earth Drawing Palm (*Zhi Tian Hua Di Zhang*) opens, stimulates and strengthens the *Yin Qiao Mai* (Yin Heel channel), *Yang Qiao Mai* (Yang Heel channel), and Foot *Shaoyang* (Gallbladder meridian). Yin Yang Fish Palm (*Yin Yang Yue Zhang*) stimulates and opens the *Dai Mai* (Belt vessel), and *Bao Mai* (Wrapper vessel). The Millstone Pushing Palm (*Tui Mo Zhang*) stimulates, opens and strengthens the *Yang Wei Mai* (Yang Linking vessel) and *Yin Wei Mai* (Yin linking vessel). The Peach Offering Palm (Xian Tao Zhang) stimulates the *ren mai* and *du mai* channels.

Each martial arts tradition can cite certain postures that open, stimulate, energize and strengthen specific meridians. The same can be said of each yoga *asana*, which is why both martial arts and yoga can be used for healing.

Incidentally, Master Cheng Ting-hua and Liu Bin both taught that every *baguazhang* posture, because it opens meridians within your body (which then essentially makes it spiritual practice), is attached to a deity who affords assistance with its mastery and protection from various types of harm. This means that Buddhas or Immortals will come to help ardent virtuous practitioners with the energy aspect of their practice when they are deserving and request such assistance.

For some people, *baguazhang, xingyiquan, taijiquan* and other soft martial arts are not practiced for fighting skills but to attain such spiritual and health benefits. Those who are exceptional practice to transcend the physical. The miraculous stories of extraordinary abilities in these paths are only possible by those who take the art to its limits. Those individuals always practice inner Qi work.

Your thoughts and your Qi are linked; your thoughts can guide or move your Qi just as a rider can maneuver a horse. Wherever your mind-will is directed, your Qi will arrive there. The *pratyahara* exercises of leading your Qi from place to place within your body can be used to internally wash your body parts in sequence and guide your Qi to opening up all its energy meridians. Stretching can eliminate impediments to energy flow within muscle pathways and *pratyahara* exercises can do this as well. This will give you extra martial power.

Many times you should wash your internal structures with Qi, countless revolutions per session – a thousand times is not too much, but the first time you do this your body may feel locked up the next day, which will quickly pass. Other techniques add embellishments to the basic practice such as the visualization of lights within body parts, reciting mantras or *bija* sounds which will vibrate your Qi in specific body regions, and arousing emotions to activate either Yin or Yang Qi through emotional toning. With advancement, you can focus on minute details and try variations. This is the way to cleanse the body with internal wind in order to prepare for real *nei-gong* achievement.

The lowest stage practitioner of yoga and the martial arts holds his body motionless in a position (*asana* or form) while practicing their breath work, while the higher practitioner guides their Qi internally. How much more powerful these practices become when the concentration, external breathing, and internal Qi movements are integrated with the body movements.

10
MERIDIAN TRAINING

In the martial arts and yoga, when holding stationary postures for a prolonged period of time there are several training options available.

The most frequent training technique is to abandon thoughts as much as possible so that your mind is empty, and then to continue holding your mind in formlessness while you maintain a steady posture. This mental state is similar to acting as if you were empty space without a body, yet possess acute awareness, as is practiced at the end of the white skeleton visualization technique only now you are holding a specific posture while doing this.

An "empty mind" allows for your Qi to circulate naturally without any interference caused by thoughts (since thoughts can move your Qi), and then your Qi can start flowing and clearing out its most natural circulation attendant with that posture. Your Qi circulation will strengthen after your Qi energy works through and dissolves energy blockages, adhesions and obstructions along its natural pathways. After that happens you will become able to move quicker and express power much more fully.

Usually the postures of yoga or the martial arts train you to use muscle movements and positions that do not impede the flow of Qi through your meridians. It is incorrect posture and positioning that impedes the flow of Qi within the body, which is the reason that many people never enter into the true realm of *nei-gong*.

By not holding onto thoughts that would interfere with your Qi circulation during a prolonged standing or sitting posture, this also gives Heaven, in the form of deities, Immortals, sages and Buddhas, an opportunity to lend you divine aid to help you open up your Qi channels. This is why some masters tell students to recite special mantras during training practices, which is because those mantras request such aid and assistance.

A second option is to simply concentrate on feeling the Qi of the muscles, limbs or body sections being stretched and strained during this time, which because of that concentrated effort to feel the muscles will help bring more Qi into the regions. This is equivalent to holding onto the Qi of a body section with concentration, but in this case you are doing so while maintaining a stationary *asana* or martial arts form that is stretching, stimulating or opening certain muscles, meridians, and Qi pathways.

A third option is to try to mentally lead your Qi throughout your body circuits while holding yourself still in a stationary posture. By means of intention or willpower, you mentally lead your Qi to move throughout your body along well-established meridian pathways or connected muscle sequences so that it penetrates your four limbs and torso along the pathways that you choose, such as those which express power.

A fourth option is to cultivate innate personality and character traits during your stationary posture when those virtues or values are connected with an organ of the Qi channels being stimulated. In this way you will help to open up the organ's Qi meridians while cultivating both your Yin and Yang Qi, and will also reinforce the development of good character traits in your life.

Each physical posture in ordinary athletics will affect different muscles and therefore different Qi meridians or groups of meridians.

However, special martial arts postures and yoga *asanas* go beyond this. They can actually help you cure illnesses and health problems because they can stimulate your Qi flow in a more dramatic way. While different *qi-gong* exercises and pranayama techniques are good for curing specific illnesses, because they can direct Qi flow certain yoga *asanas* and martial arts postures can help in these efforts too.

In yoga and the martial arts, different exercises will help improve body alignments, improve your physical constitution, heal injuries and sickness, correct internal organ imbalances, protect your health, and extend your life. What you can accomplish depends on the positions you use, what you mentally do while holding them, and how long or frequently you practice.

According to Chinese medicine, particular postures or movements can also activate specific organ Qi meridians. Our internal organs are associated with the manifestations of specific emotions such as joy (heart), anger (liver), sadness (lungs), fear (kidneys), and determination (stomach). Due to these relationships between organs and emotions, which vibrate your Qi in a certain way, you can use these *neijia* facts in your training to help open up muscle meridians for better Qi flow.

The big secret is that you *must* cultivate both your Yin Qi and Yang Qi throughout your training rather than just Yang Qi alone. By arousing a particular organ-related emotion and enveloping yourself in the feeling of the associated Qi while holding a posture that specifically stimulates and strengthens the related organ meridian, you will thereby improve your Qi flow in that meridian. If you do this enough times, the pathways will become clear and the Qi flow will improve permanently.

You can do such exercises using both the positive (Yang) and negative (Yin) emotions related to a meridian in order to increase its ability to transfer Yin and Yang Qi. Different emotions will give rise to different Qi vibrational influences (since the chemical communications unleashed convert into sensations felt by many cells of the body), and thus can help to purify your Qi and open up more Qi channels for the expression of power. From such exercises at opening up Qi channels you can develop a much greater proficiency in a form.

These facts create the opportunity for powerful training methods. In martial arts training, and in yoga, the energy pathways of your body must be cleared of circulatory blockages, bottlenecks, adhesions and obstructions so that both your Yin Qi and Yang Qi can flow smoothly throughout your muscles. To accomplish this you can train by holding the feeling of certain Yin or Yang emotions within your body as a whole while progressing through the forms or holding a static position. This works because emotions will produce internal sensations that will vibrate your body's Qi according to their nature, and hence those Yin or Yang vibrations can help you open up Yin or Yang Qi channels that you are trying to stimulate through exercise.

In particular, you should voluminously stimulate emotions to affect the organs and meridians (and limbs containing the meridians) being stimulated by a position or movement. You can do this while holding a stationary posture, or by progressing through the forms.

Yin and Yang Qi, the soft and strong, the empty and full, the heavy and light will both be cultivated in this way, which is essentially cellular stimulation in conjunction with muscle-meridian practice. You can also add to such efforts by voicing sounds that stimulate an organ-meridian pathway, or by visualizing a particular meridian pathway and the Qi flow along this route. You can do this while exercising your muscles and holding onto stimulating emotions also. The question then arises as to which feelings or emotions you should use.

There are emotions that stimulate each of your major organs, and they can be Yin and Yang Qi in nature. For instance, you can stimulate organ-meridian pathways by holding onto the Yin emotions connected with that organ (such as fear for the kidneys), or the Yang-type emotions (such as courage for the kidneys). You can create practice sessions that concentrate on just one emotion, or more. Here is how to do this.

For the heart and large intestine, you can match your movements and visualization of the relevant heart-pericardium meridians while concentrating on feeling the emotions of (1) joy, cheerfulness, elatedness, gloriousness, (2) loving-kindness, mercy, compassion, (3) magnificent generosity along with a tremendous giving spirit, (4) tenderness, softness, gentleness.

For the lungs and small intestine, you can match your movements and visualization of the relevant lung meridian while concentrating on feeling the emotions of (1) vibrancy and inspirational energy projected into the environment, (2) tolerance, acceptance, and vast openness to others, (3) strict personal honesty, truthfulness, and integrity in expression, (4) pristine mental focus and clarity.

For the stomach and spleen, you can match your movements and visualization of the relevant stomach-spleen meridians while concentrating on feeling the emotions of (1) steady resolve, willpower and self-discipline, (2) modesty, humbleness, humility, (3) straightforwardness, standing behind one's principles, (4) stableness, steadiness, being careful.

For the liver and gall bladder, you can match your movements and visualization of the relevant liver-gall bladder meridians while concentrating on feeling the emotions of (1) bold optimism and a dynamic positive attitude, (2) kindness, benevolence, and being slow to take offence, (3) purpose, determination, perseverance in achieving a goal and moving with direction, (4) calmness, peacefulness, serenity.

For the kidneys, bladder and endocrine glands, you can match your movements and visualization of the relevant kidney-bladder meridians while concentrating on feeling the emotions of (1) confidence, courage, fearlessness, (2) suppleness, flexibility, a willingness to accept change quickly and gracefully, (3) confidently expressing oneself flawlessly and fearlessly, showing the truth of oneself in an expression of vitality, (4) mental clarity, insight, a state of presence.

For the triple warmer cultivation of three body sections (the upper, middle and lower *dantian*), in most traditions this is usually cultivated during lotus posture sitting meditation practice. Buddhists recite the Om-Ah-Hung, Om-Ah-Hum, or Om-So-Hum mantra at that time where the sounds are directed to vibrate the energy within each of the three body sections. In other words, the sound syllables are consecutively voiced so that they are particularly felt within the three separate sections of head, upper torso and lower body. Yoga uses the Hreem-Shreem-Kleem mantra, and others, to stimulate and purify the Qi in each of the three separate body sections.

There are two important points to this type of practice. First, these particular sounds are used in the mantra because they each resonate (vibrate) the Qi in a specific body segment in a special way. Second, each syllable of these mantras is to be recited within that unique corresponding body segment in such a way that the sound power fully vibrates all the Qi within it as much as possible.

In systems like *Wu Xing Qi-gong* (Five Elements Movement Qi-gong) you can practice movement exercises that attempt to directly touch the Qi circulations of the heart, liver, kidneys, stomach and lungs too. The *Chan Shu Jian* Silk Cocoon Reeling spiral movements invented by *taijiquan* master Chen Wang Ting, for instance, reinforce the Qi within the meridians, and because they prime the waist to twist and turn they particularly stimulate the kidneys. Hence, whether you are trying to affect the Qi of a meridian, body section or organ through sounds or movement you can do so.

A third additional principle is that you can add emotions to your mantra recitation in order to stimulate the Qi of a particular body segment or meridian more deeply, but the emotion should correspond to the meridian or segment. Some schools of massage have found that different emotions or thought-types correspond to different body parts, but the mostly commonly used system of correspondences is that of organs and emotions. An example is feeling great joy when concentrating on the chest region that contains the heart. If you are working on opening up meridians, you would arouse and hold onto emotions, *or even a natural emotional sound*, that would correspond to the organ connected with that meridian. The martial arts system of Har Gar is an example of this technique.

You can also arouse logical feelings appropriate for body sections rather than for meridians, and they can be different from the list of organ-emotion correspondences previously given. For instance, in reciting Ohm-Ah-Hung for the head-chest-legs triplet you might try to feel/express great mental openness and acceptance when reciting "Ohm" within your head. When reciting "Ah" you might try to feel great confidence and life energy in your chest and torso. You might try to feel great stability, power and responsibility when reciting "Hung" in a way that the sound is especially felt within your waist and legs.

The practice principle is that when vocalizing a sound it should have a natural affinity for strongly stimulating the Qi within a particular body cavity or segment. Furthermore, *you should add a little extra force to try to stimulate the Qi* of that body segment by not just using the sound power of a mantra syllable but by adding other elements to that mantra recitation such as emotions, visualization efforts, stretching movements and so forth.

In certain types of mantra practice you try to vibrate the sounds in all parts of your body as a single whole in order to undulate or stimulate the entire Qi of your body and thus purify it. However, at the same time particular mantra syllables might be aimed to feel more concentrated in one particular body segment while also vibrating the whole body. "Ohm," "Ram" and "Ah," for example, vibrate the entire body but can be localized so that they are more strongly felt in certain areas such as the chest or head.

The basic principle is to vibrate your Qi in different body segments, which will stimulate the targeted Qi area and help to purify it and open Qi route restrictions in that area. This helps to open up the Qi channels within a region, and then its Qi circulation will improve and power can be expressed more fully. Adding emotions can change the tonality or character of that Qi to become more Yin or Yang in nature, and both energies need to be cultivated. Emotional content is optional, but many types of martial arts training and spiritual training demand that you practice exercises while mentally holding onto certain internal images or emotions.

Here is an example of the many variations possible for this method.

When practicing charity during ordinary life, (when you are actually physically doing something charitable such as giving something to others out of kindness), you should try to strongly feel the emotion of giving and offering in your heart that also runs through your arms to your hands and fingers. When practicing any martial arts position that strongly stimulates the heart meridian along the arms, you would also try to arouse similar feelings of giving and generosity, or joy, positivity and cheerfulness, when holding the position. These are the Yang emotions for the heart and heart meridian while the associated Yin emotions are the softer aspects of gentleness and kindness. Once again, the basic options are (1) joy, cheerfulness, elatedness, gloriousness, (2) loving-kindness, mercy, compassion, (3) magnificent generosity along with a tremendous giving spirit, and (4) tenderness, softness, gentleness. There are even more powerful Yin emotions such as depression, but the negative Yin emotions for each organ are not being cited.

The principle is to strongly feel an emotion throughout your body, or feel it strongly expressed through the muscle pathway containing a relevant meridian, in order to cultivate the Qi of that meridian and help dissolve the Qi knots and obstructions within that pathway. According to this principle, when Taoists or Buddhists perform rituals or ceremonial services that cause them to bow, at that moment they should try to feel the emotion of reverence and humility *deeply throughout their entire body* in order to make the bowing a

Qi practice that genuinely helps their spiritual cultivation. Otherwise, without a deeper emotional content to stimulate your Qi and meridians, the bowing remains just an empty exercise that moves your body. Most rituals have a symbolic meaning, but what is critical to their performance is that you hold strong emotions during the ritualistic actions you take in order to transform your Qi. The emotions produce inner sensations that vibrate your Qi, thus washing your body internally, and this is what purifies your Qi and the Qi obstructions within you. This is how rituals and ceremonies can serve as a form of spiritual cultivation and change your personality if repeated over and over again.

When working to stimulate the liver and gall bladder meridians through martial arts or yoga practice, you can hold onto positive Yang emotions such as dynamic optimism or the feeling of purpose and determination. Holding such emotions tends to make them a stronger aspect of your personality. The more peaceful Yin emotions associated with the liver and gall bladder include being slow to take offense, and calmness or serenity. Anger, wrath, malice, irritation and hostility are some of the stronger Yin aspects related to the liver, but these are not to be taught in a book.

In some martial arts, such as Han Gar (Hung Ga), the liver meridians are actually exercised through the emotion of anger. The lung and lung meridians are stimulated and strengthened through grief rather than the more positive lung-related emotions. The Hung Gar martial arts system also uses special sounds together with particular muscular movements in an "Iron Thread set" to vibrate the body's internal organs to create tremendous internal power and energy. Its *Tit Sin Kyun* set additionally uses sounds related to such emotions for internal training, specifically "Mmmmm," "Eh," "Tek," "Ahhhh," "Waaahhh," "Hit," "He He He (laughing)," "Jaaa (crying)," "Chr," and "Hei" as well as "Sssssshhh" and "Hoh."

In this system the liver is matched with anger and shouting sounds, the heart with joy and laughing sounds, the stomach with overthinking and singing sounds, the lungs with grief and crying sounds, and the kidneys with fear and moaning sounds. Because the

Iron Thread Set combines movements with sounds, breathing patterns and emotions relevant for the specific meridians being activated, this should give you an idea of how to combine various factors for training.

Once you understand the principles of combination you can develop your own practice techniques. You are basically (1) activating an organ or its meridians by performing a physical action that stimulates a meridian, (2) simultaneously expressing emotions related to the Qi of that meridian, and (3) voicing sounds that express the emotions related to that meridian's Qi or which especially vibrate a meridian region and pathway. (4) Visualizations of the meridian can be added as well.

The whole point is to activate the Qi of a meridian and its surrounding muscle pathways in order to clear that route of any impediments that hamper better Qi flow. This is the essential basis of many spiritual practices, including *kundalini* yoga and Buddhist Vajrayana techniques. If you were to lift weights, for instance, you could similarly concentrate on the meridians being activated during your stretching and straining of muscles being exercised, and in this way cultivate your meridians and strength that will both be used in your martial arts.

In some martial arts practices, you are taught to absorb through the top of your head, or through all your pores, the Yin and Yang essences of the sun and moon in order to feed your Qi and harmonize your inner balance of energies. You would do this on special days or during certain hours of the day that correspond to the peak of these energies *if* that is also a safe time to do so. Or, you might perform these practices during the initial ascension of such energies if gentler stimulation was warranted. A teacher is necessary to guide you through such practices.

Martial artists who know Taoist principles are taught to absorb the Yin or Yang energies from celestial bodies or their environment and collect it within body cavities such as the lower *dantian*. It is expected to then disperse naturally into the depths of their bodies to reach and nourish all their cells. The Qi once absorbed will spread like a mesh throughout the body to all its tissues within the muscles, organs, and even bones.

Most people are deficient in cultivating Yin energies, so many Yin absorption techniques have been invented for devoted yoga and martial arts practitioners. Typically, individuals are taught to sometimes practice in heavy Yin areas such as graveyards or desolate locations at night since they abound with Yin Qi that is then naturally absorbed during practice sessions.

In some very esoteric practices individuals are taught to absorb the energies of planets such as Venus, Mars, Jupiter and Saturn when the planets are visible, exalted, closest to the Earth or under other unusual astronomical aspects that allow them to express their energies to the fullest. Some methods teach you to draw the energy into the crown of your head through the *baihui* point and then into the *dantian* for distribution elsewhere.

Some absorption methods even focus on absorbing the Qi of trees, mountains, lakes or rivers, and similarly involve pulling Qi through your *baihui or laogong* points into your body. If the energy is too strong it can be pushed out of your body through your *yongquan* points in the feet. In some techniques you pull Qi into the body through the *laogang* points in the palms, route it up your arms into your chest, guide it down to the lower *dantian*, next to your perineum *(huiyin)*, then up along your spine into your head and back to your chest again. The main concern of all these various techniques is always to develop the main pathways and forces of Yin and Yang inside the body.

All the special *neijia* skills in martial arts are based on developing the Yin Qi and Yang Qi capabilities within one's body, and especially developing the Qi transmission capabilities of the *dantian* because most of the body's power is routed through it. Many martial skills require you to inhale when practicing postures while also drawing Qi into your *dantian* and then dispersing it throughout all parts of your body.

Yin and Yang energies are the fundamental root behind the martial abilities of emptiness-fullness, lightness-heaviness (rootedness), and hardness-softness that are taught in many traditions. Martial artists with higher attainments commonly work at mastering such Yin-Yang transformations within themselves, especially the special skill of transforming lightness into heaviness and heaviness into lightness. If they master these powers they can even absorb the strike of a heavy blow and transform that energy into lightness through internal transformations. This is a result only achievable at the level of true *nei-gong* and *Tao-gong*.

For instance, *baguazhang* master Tung Hai-Chuan could transform a heavy strike from an opponent into lightness by drawing the fullness of the *shi jin* striking force into his *dantian* and nullifying the heaviness into *xu jin*, a force with the quality of lightness and emptiness. This was due to his mastery of *qing gong*, or lightness development, which is actually the *laghima siddhi* of yoga that you only attain when you achieve an immortal Srotapanna deva body due to inner cultivation work. Wang Shujin, who was a master of *baguazhang, taijiquan and xingyiquan*, could absorb heavy strikes with no damage as well.

The absorption practices for Yin and Yang energies are actually aimed at training practitioners in the special yoga abilities of *garima siddhi* (heaviness) and *laghima siddhi* (lightness). These are two of the traditional eight yoga siddhis that are possible when someone gains control over their inner subtle body composed of Qi.

These eight yoga siddhis are the basis of many special martial arts skills. When making efforts to master these skills, sometimes martial artists will practice simultaneously making one palm hard and the other open and soft, and then reversing, or making the upper part of their body feel light, open and expansive while the lower part feels heavy like it is contracting and uniting inwardly. Qi lightness practice that does not become floatingness can give you agility whereas Qi sinking (weightedness) practice that does not turn into heaviness can give you firmness.

The principle to recognize is that there are many ways to practice stationary standing (or sitting) postures other than just remaining in mental stillness during motionlessness. You can also choose more active routes that entail circulating your inner energy while you hold an immobile position, or stimulating your internal energies in various ways connected with emotions, visualizations, sounds and so forth.

While the inner energies can be coordinated with various emotions, which can help heal your inner organs and open up related Qi meridians and muscular force Qi pathways, the basis of all these practices is Yin and Yang Qi that can expressed in various ways and tonalities.

11
CULTIVATING YOUR YIN AND YANG QI

As stated, a little known principle in yoga and the martial arts is that you must cultivate your Yin Qi as well as your Yang Qi. Most people only focus on cultivating their Yang Qi, which is commonly known as "*kundalini*," and totally neglect Yin Qi cultivation. Spiritual masters, however, will put students into extreme Yin Qi environments (such as cemeteries or ossuaries) or Yin Qi stimulation or absorption situations so that they can cultivate their Yin Qi without being aware of the process.

YIN QI

Your Yin Qi is normally stimulated by the emotions of fear, anxiety, worry, forlornness, loneliness, embarrassment, humiliation, shame, regret, remorse, guilt, sadness, helplessness, hopelessness, depression, grief, despair, disgust, repugnance, despising, sneakiness, greediness, craving, hate, an awareness of loss, and revenge. However, softness, humility, obedience, openness, patience, yielding and acceptance also involve your Yin Qi as well.

Yin Qi is most often associated with great fright and anxiety (and thus the kidneys), which is why many spiritual masters will actually put their students into situations of great fear and worry, on purpose, in order to stimulate and then purify the Yin essences of their inner subtle body. Any experiences that raise these "negative" emotions will stimulate your Yin Qi.

Many religions request of followers that they regularly review and reflect upon their behavior in order that individuals correct their personality faults, such as harmful aggressive tendencies, and also so that adherents purify their Yin Qi on a regular basis. Individuals are taught to first discover and then confess their recent personal errors and faults, and then asked to show contrition and repentance. A regular practice of reviewing your behavioral, confessing faults to a higher power and showing repentance will consistently help you to purify your Yin Qi. It will also stimulate the passive Yin emotions of humbleness and humility that we all need in order to counteract excessive Yang Qi tendencies in our personalities.

Various activities or environments may cause your body to feel Yin Qi as well because they stir up Yin emotions or because they expose you to Yin Qi in the environment. This includes visiting graves, scary forests, limestone formations, deserted desolate places, cold weather, going outside during the pitch black of night, darkness retreats, training under a cold waterfall, or feeling the lunar energies of a full moon. When you are sick with a cold or flu this is a Yin situation too, especially if you feel chills. Working in an ossuary, funeral home, crematorium, or visiting graves are activities that will also expose you to a lot of Yin energy that you can absorb if you remain long enough. If you place water in a bottle that is coated internally with silver nitrate (a silver mirrored flask), the evaporating water that escapes will usually feel very cool because of the water's Yin nature.

Ingesting cooling herbs, cold minerals or cooling drinks will tend to stimulate your body's Yin Qi. The thoughts of death, sickness, evil, loss, purgatory, Hell, ghosts, or demons will also cause your Yin Qi to stir, partly because they stimulate fear. Many countries have holidays that stimulate Yin Qi on a national scale too such as Tomb Sweeping Day in China, *Dia de Muertos* in Mexico or Halloween in America. Criminal activities such as stealing, the experience of pain or torture, attending a séance or seeing witchcraft can also stimulate your Yin Qi. During sickness when you feel chills or have cold sweats your Yin Qi is also active.

Buddhism uses the vehicle of the *Vimalakirti Sutra* to explain that people who wish to cultivate their Qi and purify their inner subtle body, which is a necessity for the highest level of martial arts, must absolutely stimulate and transform their Yin Qi so that it becomes free of defilements. You cannot just cultivate the ascension of Yang Qi alone. This is one of the top secrets of the higher martial arts, which is that you must cultivate or absorb Yin Qi in order to balance your Yang Qi since it usually becomes too excessive, and you must purify the Yin Qi inside yourself.

In the Buddhist *Vimalakirti Sutra* the student Shariputra experiences a "goddess flower lesson" within enlightened layman Vimalakirti's small ten-foot square room. Many Buddhas and Bodhisattvas shrink themselves down and enter into this small room, which symbolizes accomplished spiritual masters (of the Srotapanna level and higher) using their etheric Qi-bodies to enter Shariputra's brain. They exhibit the shrinking yogic power of the *anima siddhi* that is a natural capability of everyone's subtle body, just as are the martial arts skills of lightness and heaviness. Shariputra at that time is going through a twelve-year transformation process to strengthen his inner Qi-body and purify it of defilements so that he can finally attain the subtle body that constitutes the initial Arhat stage of achievement, and during this lesson feels as if his male gender is changed into that of a female. This feeling of feminization happens because the Buddhas present stimulate his Yin Qi through a possession practice of *ishita siddhi* or "lordship over someone," and cause him to feel like he is a girl. Nothing actually happens to his sexual organs (in terms of losing them or their turning into a vagina). It is just that he feels "Yin all over."

In epic legends from around the world, the greatest masculine heroes of athletic fame often undergo gender switching experiences just like this in order to teach the principle that the highest levels of athletic achievement require Yin Qi purification. For example, the Greco-

Roman hero Hercules (the son of Zeus) was forced to dress in women's clothing and perform women's work for a period of one year, which is what the Indian sage Ramakrishna did to purify and transform his Yin Qi. In the great Indian epic *Mahabharata,* the great martial hero Arjuna, whose name means "shining" or "brightness," had to act like a eunuch and wear women's clothing for one year of Yin Qi feminization as well. At one time, the Thunder God Thor also had to dress in women's clothing in order to retrieve his hammer that was in the possession of a powerful giant.[17] Only after he did this could he retrieve his hammer Mjolnir, which symbolized his Yang Qi. In all cases the mental and physical state of feeling very Yin like a female is temporary and used only for the purpose of purifying and transforming your Yin Qi energies.

Reciting the mantras of female Buddhas or deities, or performing their ritual ceremonies that invite their presence and purification work on your body, are ways to cultivate your Yin Qi for the martial arts. This also includes reciting the mantra of the Hell Buddha Ksitigarbha – who deals with hells, sickness, death and the dying – and the mantras of Yama, the Indian God of Death. Sadhanas involving lunar light, water visualizations, cold water activities, darkness retreats, and the practice of Yin-animal forms in the martial arts while feeling the Yin Qi of the animal, are also ways to cultivate your Yin Qi.

Just as the various phases of the moon represent different intensities of Yin Qi that can be absorbed by martial artists, the ten Mahavidyas

---

[17] You can read of many cultivation tales where men became women and women became men in *Shikhandi*, by Devdutt Pattanaik. These are not real physical transformations but just mental absorptions of having feminine Qi. Of note is the story of the Greek man Tiresias who was "changed into a woman" due to the actions of the goddess Hera. This occurred after he struck two copulating snakes, which symbolizes that he was cultivating the Yin and Yang Qi of his body. Later he regained his masculinity and was given the gift of prophecy, the ability to understand bird song, and a lifespan of seven lives, indicating that he had purified his inner subtle body and become an Arhat. Tiresias could mediate between the gods and humans, and his story with all the special powers is essentially a Greek tale hinting at the subtle body attainment.

of Hinduism represent different types of Yin Qi that can be aroused within yourself as a form of cultivation practice when you mentally identify yourself with the deity. There is Kali who represents wild, uncontrollable Yin Qi; Bhairavi whose Yin Qi is fierce, frightful, and terrifying; Tripura Sundari who represents the smooth Yin Qi of a beautiful woman; Matangi who represents the graceful Yin Qi of an artistic woman; Tara who represents the Yin Qi of a gentle, compassionate woman; Bhuvaneshvari who represents the Yin Qi of a caring mother; Chinnamasta who represents the Yin Qi of a woman who absolutely sacrifices herself for others; Kamala who represents the Yin Qi of a wealthy female patron who provides blessings to others; Bagalamukhi who represents Yin Qi strong enough to control enemies; and Dhumavati who represents dark, inauspicious, bad fortune Yin Qi.

India also has tantric practices for Saraswati (artistic Yin Qi), Devi (motherly Yin Qi), Durga (protective Yin Qi), Gauri (young girl Qi), and many more feminine forces. The tantric sadhanas (ceremonies that affect your Qi) are ways to cultivate various degrees of your Yin Qi when you identify with such types of Yin Qi during the devotional acts. Different animal styles of martial arts are supposed to also arouse different types of Yin Qi (or Yang Qi) within you as well, particularly when you are imitate the feeling of being a Yin-type animal when practicing that form's martial arts movements.

In the Aghori tradition of India, future yogis are ordered to perform frightening ceremonies (sadhanas) with dead bodies, in cemeteries, and at midnight in order to stimulate their Yin Qi. The Aghori tradition is renown for its various frightening and seemingly anti-social practices. Often they are simply strong Yin Qi cultivation methods for those destined to attain enlightenment if they work hard at cultivating their body's Qi through a large variety of other practices as well.

The reason all these unusual methods are mentioned is because you should understand the principle that there are many ways to cultivate your Yin Qi, and you absolutely must do this for the highest levels of yoga and martial arts. Sometimes top martial arts masters engage in seemingly mysterious practices that are just a method of Yin Qi absorption or purification that is part of their personal *neijiaquan*. A simple example is that many top martial artists practice Qi absorption techniques late at night when the earth's Yin Qi is fullest. Because of its dominance the earth's Yin Qi can be more easily absorbed into the body at that time, so it is a good time to work at mastering heavy or crushing forces.

The point is that you must cultivate both Yang Qi and Yin Qi at the highest level of martial arts, but most practitioners become confused and typically only work at cultivating their Yang Qi, which often leads to sickness and imbalance.

For instance, in the *Surangama Sutra* of Buddhism there was a monk named Ucchusma who was plagued by sexual desire and therefore frequently lost his Jing (semen) and Qi through masturbation even though their retention is necessary for cultivation. In Chinese culture, preserving one's Jing and Qi inside your body is considered the same as preserving valuable treasures. Vowing to change his habit of sexual loss, Ucchusmma engaged in tremendous pranayama exercises along with sexual restraint while envisioning that his body became a mass of raging fire. As a consequence of cultivation efforts that made him become too Yang, he developed a red countenance due to the Qi energies rising to his head, and was nicknamed "Fire Head" as a result.

Similarly, the wrathful, angry countenances of guardian deities ("protection gods") who grace many Buddhist temples indicates that they have cultivated a lot of strong Yang Qi, and are ready to use their martial abilities to oppose evil and protect the temple.

In India there is also the story of the Hindu seer Rishyashringa, a strict yogi who never broke his celibacy and thus never lost his semen through ejaculation. A drought and then famine appeared in his land that was attributed to his personal cultivation work. The drought was attributed to him because the lack of rain symbolized that he was only cultivating ascending Yang Qi like Ucchusma, and thus depleting (burning away) his Yin essence. Without sufficient Yin Qi to counterbalance the accumulation of Yang Qi, the circulation of Yin Qi through your meridians will suffer and in particular the descending Qi circulation down your front channel will become deficient.

You need to cultivate both Yang Qi and Yin Qi on the spiritual path and need to open both Yin and Yang meridians. With celibacy and Yang Qi cultivation your Qi ascends to your head, but for proper internal circulation your Qi must flow everywhere freely. It must also descend from your head to your *dantian* and perineum, which is a pathway often associated with Yin Qi. The microcosmic circulation within the body therefore recycles Qi in a circular orbit of Yang Qi going up the spine and Yin Qi coming down the front of the body. This is just like nature which causes lake water to evaporate and ascend upwards to become clouds, which then precipitate rain out of fullness, and then that water falls to the ground to feed the lakes and streams from which it came. Thus water, like the Qi within our body, returns to its source by traveling a circular pathway of up and down.

After ascending to your brain, your Qi circulation descends through the *ren mai* conception channel in the front of your body, which is called the water channel, as well as through the pathway of your digestive organs that most people neglect in their cultivation work. Since Rishyashringa was only cultivating Yang Qi accumulation and ascension through ardent celibate yoga practices, he was neglecting the accumulation and circulation of Yin Qi throughout his body that must also penetrate all its tissues. Just as the rain produced by evaporation must fall from the skies after accumulation and return to earth's lakes and streams, nature's way is that you cannot just cultivate your Yang Qi or you will become sick or imbalanced.

In the story, the king of the region therefore sends a courtesan to seduce Rishyashringa into having sex, which represents balancing his Yang Qi with Yin Qi. After ejaculation and the consequential descent of his own internal Qi from coupling with the Yin Qi maiden, the sky breaks and bountiful rains fall from the heavens to restore the kingdom. The drought is broken when Yin and Yang are restored to their proper balance.

In short, both your Yin Qi and Yang Qi must undergo purification of defilements along the pathway of the martial arts. You cannot cultivate just Yang Qi alone.

YANG QI

Your Yang Qi normally arises due to the emotions of anger, pride, courage or bravery, confidence, triumph, enthusiasm, euphoria, exhilaration, joy, happiness, mirth, thrills, cheerfulness, optimism, love, willpower, determination, the feeling of strength and aliveness. Blissful flow states are characterized by Yang Qi whereas more refined states of flow are characterized by balanced Yin and Yang forces within you.

Yang Qi is stimulated during active exercise, athletic sports, fighting, sexual excitement, attendance at happy festivals or ceremonies such as weddings, and masculinity practices. Meditation practice, sunshine visualizations, pranayama cultivation, etcetera are all activities used to raise and cultivate the Yang Qi of your body. If you listen to pep talks, as is done in sports locker rooms during competitive matches, this is an example of listening to a message to raise your Yang Qi while another simple way to raise your Qi is to open your eyes wide and simply recite any words that raise your vitality of spirit.[18]

Ingesting heating herbs and eating spicy food will also stimulate your

---

[18] Sounds (such as voices or music) can put you to sleep, calm your mind or raise your spirit. They can stimulate plant growth, milk production, and readily change our emotions that, in turn, will affect our Qi due to the inner sensations they cause. Because of their effect on our Qi, they are used in countless cultivation techniques because their tones can vibrate (stimulate) the Qi channels within our bodies and unlock the potential of our Qi by vibrating away Qi flow restrictions.

Yang Qi. Garlic, onions, leeks, scallions and shallots eaten cooked are said to raise your sexual desires because they stimulate Yang Qi, so are avoided by celibate monks and nuns in many spiritual traditions. If eaten raw they are said to increase your anger, which is also a sign of excessive or uncontrolled Yang Qi. Stimulating the emotion of anger will also flood your body's tissues with Yang Qi.

In Tibetan Buddhism, monks and nuns are actually taught to envision that they become a wrathful deity like Yamantaka in order to raise their Yang Qi. Taking the Scandinavian Thunder God Thor as a *yidam*, or the Greek sun god Apollo, and imagining that you transform into them or some other Yang Qi deity during meditation will do so as well. When you undergo meditation practices where you identify yourself with a *yidam* deity (such as Yamantaka, Vajrayogini, Chakrasamvara, Kalachakra, Hevajra, Guhyasamaja. Hayagriva, Kalachakra, Kurukulla, Tara, Vajrakilaya, etcetera) for the purposes of spiritual "transformation," this is essentially *nei-gong* Qi practice to stimulate your Yang Qi so that it becomes energized or impregnated with the nature of the Qi of the deity's character you imagine as your role-model. Typically for such practices you recite a mantra (sometimes at many different locations throughout your body, or upon special acupuncture points) to stimulate your Qi for opening up Qi meridians, or in order to request Qi aid from masters who have previously achieved enlightenment via the same technique of practice.

Tibetan Buddhism has a number of *yidam* practices that involve identifying yourself with wrathful deities, which is called "divine pride." The mental aspects of such practices, done incorrectly, will tend to produce residues of arrogance, anger, pride, rudeness, domineering and fighting in your personality. The types of emotions and thoughts you practice generating and holding onto during *yidam* practices (in order to raise your Yin Qi or Yang Qi), which are similar to the bhakti devotional practices within other spiritual traditions, will to some extent impress your Qi with those same characteristics. The warning is that you do not want arrogance and aggressive tendencies to become a permanent feature of your personality. A tree branch bends in time from its own weight, so be careful not to pile onto yourself unwanted characteristics that are not virtues.

The purpose of such practices is to cultivate and thus purify from defilements your Qi and its circulatory pathways. Then your Qi will flow more smoothly within you, which will help bring the flow state within closer reach. This is why you cultivate both the Yin Qi and Yang Qi of your body that predominate in different meridian pathways.

Essentially, the spiritual practices within most religions are basically various yogas for cultivating your personality and Qi over time. The same objective of transforming your character and Qi can be claimed by any of the soft martial arts schools. All the talk about emptiness, consciousness, original nature, bliss and so on found in the spiritual schools offering "enlightenment teachings" comes down to doing special forms of yoga (especially pranayama, *qi-gong* and *nei-gong*) in order to first purify the Qi of the energy matrix that runs throughout your physical body so that it becomes strengthened, purified (free of defilements), loosens its adhesion to your physical nature, and then can gain an independence where it can pop out of your physical body at will. That emergence out of your physical body is of an independent spiritual body composed of your Qi energy, and is the first stage of "spiritual enlightenment." The achievement anoints you as a Srotapanna or Taoist immortal.

The reason that yoga and the martial arts use physical stretching and movements as a spiritual practice is because this is the easiest and quickest route to opening up all the Qi pathways within your body, by untangling their knots and impediments, so that your body's inner Qi circulation loses all its bottlenecks and obstructions that then makes it possible for this event to happen. As your Qi moves through the restrictions within the body, it slowly dissolves those blockages through repeated circulations.

Needless to say, yoga and the martial arts have health and longevity benefits if you don't succeed in the transcendental attainments, as well as benefits for training your mind, attitudes and personal discipline. They can teach you courage, confidence, discipline, hard work, focus, etiquette and a good temperament. They are a fundamental way of improving yourself through a type of training that offers a unique educational potential. They are a form of character development and self-improvement training that require you to do your best every day and to improve upon that every day. Hence they necessitate error correction of yourself. They are a way of becoming a better version of yourself.

Some use martial arts for fighting, and some use it for self-improvement. Many people consider them only a method for training how to fight, but martial arts train your mind, skills, spirit, conduct and morality. They are actually a physical skills training system that offers you a means of mastering your body, mind and spirit. They are a training method of self-perfection that is actually focused on helping you conquer yourself rather than conquer others. Thus they are worthwhile even if you don't obtain the immortal fruit.

Typically Tibetan monks cultivate their Yang Qi through special visualization and breathing practices, called *tummo* meditation, and are tested in wintery contests where they must sit in icy cold weather and melt the snow around them. Indian sadhus, on the other hand, are tested on their Yin Qi internal cooling powers by sitting in the hot sun surrounded by burning piles of cow dung while a pot of burning dung also sits atop their head. For the mountain monks of Japanese *Shugendo*, their ability to control their Yin Qi and Yang Qi is tested during exercises of standing under freezing waterfalls and walking over hot coals. All sorts of practices are seen across the world that test your abilities to manipulate your Yin Qi and Yang Qi.

Physical exercises such as the martial arts and yoga, as well as fire visualization meditations and *kundalini* yoga, are typical Yang Qi cultivation methods. The four Buddhist emotional immeasurable practices of infinite joy, kindness, compassion and equanimity are also methods to help you cultivate your Yang Qi. By dwelling in infinite emotions, this activity will penetrate and transform all the Qi of your body because you are making the emotions as big as possible and becoming that characteristic. Emotions create sensations within the body that vibrate its Qi, and thus your Qi will become impregnated with those Yang characteristics, thus transforming it. Normally you should just let emotional energy move through your system until it completes itself, which is "detachment," but here you hold onto it with stability in order to change the character of your Qi and temperament.

If you continually practice this over time, you will slowly change your personality to develop in the direction of those personality dispositions. You will also impregnate or imprint your cells with those same emotional energies. This is proven by the fact that organ transplant recipients often develop some of the personality traits of their donors. Hence, Qi cultivation can definitely change your personality.

Therefore you can also practice cultivating emotions such as tremendous (immeasurable) courage, valor, vigor, generosity, authority, positive energy, stamina, mirth, and so forth to cultivate your Yang Qi, which will start to flavor your Qi and change your predispositions through this toning process. By engendering large emotions and holding those emotional states in mind and body it is like meat soaking in a sauce that gradually permeates it with flavor. Through the force of permeation over a long period of time you will slowly affect the Qi of your body, your thoughts and finally your conduct. This can be used as a remedy for personality defects and as a means for developing virtuous qualities.

To make greatest use of this technique, during practice sessions (or during daily idle moments such as waiting in line somewhere) you should imagine suffusing, permeating, perfuming or saturating yourself with the Qi or aura of the character trait you strongly wish to cultivate, imagine also projecting it into your outer environment, and simultaneously try to *feel the Qi of that characteristic within you and everywhere*. You might even engage in repeating affirmations that help you raise and maintain that large Qi aura.

This short synopsis gives an idea of some of the Yin Qi and Yang Qi cultivation practices that monks and nuns use to raise and purify their Yin Qi and Yang Qi of defilements. Some of them can be repeated by yogis and martial artists with the point being that you must cultivate both your Yin Qi and Yang Qi. Spiritual schools improvise on techniques according to principle, varying on their techniques but targeting the same outcome. Ultimately you must learn yin-yang coordination within yourself and within your techniques whether they are from the martial arts or yoga.

Altogether you have now seen techniques that work on the Qi of your muscles, organs and bones; meridians or Qi circulatory orbits; muscle force transmission pathways; *bindus* or acupuncture points; appendages such as arms and legs; internal organs; body cavities such as the three *dantian*, chakra sections and other sectioning schemes; and parts (such as the ears, eyes, penis and so forth). You normally learn how to cultivate the Qi within all these sections via body alignments in yoga and the martial arts, and via specific body motions. However, you have gone beyond such fundamental teachings by also learning how to stimulate and cultivate your Qi via breathing, visualization, sounds or sound vibrations, lights, mental states, emotions, willpower guidance of movement, prayers or mantras that request aid, and absorption. The mind is the king, so you need to know in your mind how to cultivate these various techniques to purify your Yin and Yang Qi to progress to higher achievement levels.

Yogis and martial artists typically share many of the same techniques that draw upon these principles. Their common repertoire of techniques includes the stillness practice or empty mind meditation. However, the unique aspect to these two schools is that they use physical movements and inner Qi exercises to attain quicker results in Qi purification and transformation than that offered by devotional religious practices such as temple worship. Once you understand these principles, this knowledge should enable you to adapt your practices and take them to a higher level.

12
UNIFYING YOUR MIND AND QI

The goal of *neijia* yoga is to fully express your Qi throughout your body, especially your limbs, and to be able to use your Qi effectively in movement and martial activities.

The practice of martial arts starts with *wai-gong* exercises that condition your muscles, ligaments, and tendons. Through the practice of forms you train your body so that it can perform movements that allow you to exert force effectively. You learn special body alignments and how to exert force correctly in a variety of different ways. Naturally, you learn tactical positioning along with optimal body mechanics for self-protection and for exerting force against opponents.

External physical practice both energizes and builds the muscles in your body so that they can move in ways that manifest maximum speed and strength. You condition your body to do so by learning the forms correctly, just as you learn yoga *asanas* in order to open up all your Qi pathways to increase your Qi circulation for its fullest expression. Yoga is excellent for opening up Qi pathways, but its teachings are deficient as to methods for Qi expression through movement.

For maximum strength and speed in the martial arts, you must go beyond simple mechanical skills and learn how to exert force in conjunction with your breathing. You must connect the expression of the breath with the application of strength by undertaking drills to coordinate your breathing with your movements. This is why each posture in *taijiquan* has its own *qi-gong* practice, or special way of breathing. In fact, in the martial arts community virtually every style has its own set of *qi-gong* breath training techniques.

For this objective of learning better breathing you start by learning pranayama and performing *qi-gong* exercises, which will make your breathing more balanced and efficient. These exercises will add power to your breath. Just through simple breathing exercises alone you can learn to move better and pack your internal tissues (muscles) with more Qi. The *qi-gong* methods that emphasize the physical body more will improve the Qi circulation within the areas being exercised and the physical strength of those areas.

For even greater ability you need to go beyond the superficial level of Qi in your body that pranayama and *qi-gong* deals with and learn how to build up and circulate your real Qi. Then you can energize your muscles past the ordinary levels of maximum power. Therefore, progressive training next focuses on circulating and building up your real Qi internally, which requires you to maintain correct breathing patterns, body alignments and to learn relaxation and softness to some degree. This holds true even for the hard martial arts.

Imagine that the Qi within your body is like water running through a large network of countless rivers, tributaries, streams and even irrigation ditches that nourish all the cells of your body. In order to keep the water running smoothly, the rivers on through the ditches must be regularly cleared of obstructions, which is why we frequently dredge lakes and rivers. Similarly, to improve your Qi circulation by making Qi flow more fluid you must engage in a variety of different internal *nei-gong* exercises that work deeper than *qi-gong* to clear your Qi pathways of obstructions.

Traditionally, you first start with opening the "microcosmic circulation" of Qi that runs up your spine and down the front of your body, which is through your *du mai* and *ren mai* channels, and then you can engage in more elaborate Qi exercises. To better express Qi through your martial arts, you must practice in a variety of specialized postures, breath work and internal energy exercises that collectively cleanse your tissues, enable you to accumulate Qi internally, improve internal Qi circulation so that it is free of bottlenecks, and enable you to optimally lead your Qi to your limbs and throughout your body as a whole. Yoga tries to accomplish this through stretches and pranayama, but doesn't teach the deeper *neijia* practices unless you enter the realms of *kundalini* or *kriya yoga*.

The standard sequence of practice is as follows. First, you train your muscles and tendons for strength, endurance, speed and elasticity. Next, you work on your training your breathing styles. Then you build up a foundation of Qi within your body from your head to the bottom of your feet through various internal exercises that wash your muscles, organs and pathways. The purpose is to eliminate impediments and bottlenecks to your internal Qi flow that will thereby improve your internal Qi circulation and also allow you to store more Qi inside your body. Generally speaking, external or "hard" martial arts start by training strength and later practice Qi whereas the "soft" or internal styles focus on developing Qi energy first and physical strength later.

The ultimate target is to make your Qi circulate smoother and more easily throughout your body, which will produce a deeper level of physical strength and more profound (Qi flow related) states of mental clarity. Then you must learn how to lead the Qi to your muscles and tendons during training, which will both energize them and transform them so that they function more efficiently. You must learn how to guide your Qi internally and coordinate its circulation with forms and movements so that the two become unified as one. You must do this in conjunction with appropriate breathing, which takes devoted work. Breathing can be considered a "strategy" that lets you lead your Qi effectively.

By working on muscles first and Qi second, you first train that which has shape and then that which has no shape. You train muscles externally, and train Qi internally. Then you practice combining the two until they become one.

In order that your shape does not impede the circulation of formless Qi inside you, the way in which you hold and express your body must be of a special alignment that does not impede your Qi flow, but which also allows for the maximum exertion of speed and force. Without an internal alignment conducive to your Qi, martial arts are just motion. Therefore you must start on this road by mastering *asanas*, martial arts forms and physical movements. You must learn how to correctly utilize the muscles of your body while maintaining a very proper and specific body alignment that does not inhibit the flow of your Qi. When proceeding with movements, you must then practice coordinating your movements with your breath.

Many practitioners cannot freely express Qi because their postures or movements are flawed. If your body parts are not properly aligned then power cannot be easily transmitted. Therefore once again, you must start by mastering the forms and physical movements. This is true in both yoga and the martial arts. A focus on breathing comes next, then an emphasis on manipulating your superficial Qi, and finally mastery of your true internal energy.

You must learn how to correctly utilize the muscles of your body while maintaining a proper body alignment, and then connect your breathing and the circulation of your Qi with your movements. If the alignments are off then your Qi will not match fully. Therefore, learn how to coordinate your Qi circulation with forms, which starts by matching your breathing with your forms. Since your breath can move your Qi, you must practice pranayama and *qi-gong* exercise in order to learn how to optimize and regulate your breath within your muscles. When you reach the realm of being able to lead your Qi, you must work on enhancing your ability to circulate Qi and direct it to different areas of your body. The more you refine your training the more you will advance.

The principle behind all this training is that the mind can lead Qi to the muscles so that they have more speed and power. If you can train your muscles and develop your Qi and Qi pathways, you will be able to energize your muscles to a higher level and increase your fighting effectiveness. Another effect is that the Qi circulation within your body becomes more perfect. This is the basis of becoming a spiritual Immortal.

If your Qi circulation becomes smooth, it is as if your body is forgotten. The body can be ignored, the mind becomes peaceful and awareness becomes clear and bright without extraneous noise in the head. Optimal breathing patterns and Qi circulation can let you taste the state of flow, whereas forgetting your body because it is so healthy and its energy flows are so proficient enables you to taste the bliss of "no extremities" or "no mind and no body."

13
THE TRANSCENDENTAL SEQUENCE
OF PROGRESSION

From *wai-gong* to *qi-gong*, *nei-gong* and then *Tao-gong*, this is the sequence of progress for mastering your internal energy.

You first work on stretching or developing your muscles, postures and movements, and then regulating your breath through breathing practices until a new pattern becomes natural. Regulation stops when you reach the stage of no regulation being necessary.

Next, you practice deeper pranayama exercises to gain control of your breath. Through these exercises you should increase your breath retention skills as well as your lung capacity. You will start opening up more Qi channels due to prolonged breath retention, and increase the power of your breath that later can be used for powerful martial abilities. Celibacy at times is necessary during this training, for if your Qi is lost due to its ejaculation along with semen, where will be the pressurized energy necessary for forcing open up your Qi channels and meridians?

From gaining control of your breath and cleansing some Qi channels, you next start grabbing hold of and moving a superficial level of your Qi force. Your breathing moves your superficial Qi in *qi-gong* practices whereas your mind moves your real Qi in *nei-gong* practices. In *qi-gong* you just start to form a connection between your mind and your Qi, and in *nei-gong* you solidify and stabilize a real mind-body connection between the two so that you can truly lead your deepest Qi with your mind. This is a true spiritual unity. *Qi-gong* practice, on the other hand, truly only deals with the superficial wind element of your body.

After gaining proficiency in using your breathing to move your Qi, now you should use your will to lead your Qi around inside you. Wash all your tissues, open up all your pathways, rotate your Qi everywhere in logical patterns that follow the shape of body structures or which match with your movements. *Qi-gong*, because it depends on the breath, moves from the outside to the inside whereas *nei-gong* depends on the mind and taps the deepest inside to conjoin with the outside.

You should then strive to reach a level where you can simultaneously control multiple mind-body Qi movements by energizing and managing the Qi flows of your entire system at one time. The objective is to gain access to the energy of your totality where body, mind and spirit integrate and the "whole you" functions as a single body of flowing energy. If you can unite your whole Qi as one and manifest it as power, this is called "gaining" in martial arts because you have gained the secret. This is how you progress beyond mere physical technique.

From the stage of grabbing control of your internal energy and manipulating its transformations, next you must ignite your *kundalini* (the deepest real Qi of your body) and undergo a twelve-year process of transformation.

Sun Wu-Kong had a staff, Hanuman had a mace, Hercules had a club, Thor had a hammer. All these weapons symbolize their owner's Qi. They symbolize the fact that the hero attained mastery over his vital energy and internal power – their Qi. Mind merges with energy, energy produces strength. When you master the previous practices, you will gain such power.

If you start mastering your Qi and reach the real practice of *nei-gong*, a twelve-year process of deep transformation will commence overseen by the Buddhas, deities and Immortals. At this stage, one should continue their practice with a good teacher in a quiet location away from society. In time your Qi will differentiate into true Yin and Yang, and your energy will eventually become like sunlight, which is actually composed of different colors. It is said that a good sword can cut sunlight and leave a rainbow in its place. Upon an Arhat's attainment of full enlightenment, the secret of this principle can be known.

The enlightenment of the Buddhists, as well as Taoists and yogis, is initially the Srotapanna achievement, which is the fact that your subtle body of Qi can leave your physical body at will. The yoga sutras say that it has eight *siddhi*s or miraculous abilities, which include the lightness and heaviness capabilities demonstrated by the greatest martial artists. Martial artists can display these feats because they have achieved (at least) the Srotapanna Arhat body of enlightenment, which means they have become Taoist Immortals because their spirits can leave their physical shells. There are higher attainment levels beyond this initial level of accomplishment.

The way to the achievement is not to solely concentrate on your muscles, but to also focus on your internal energy until your inner subtle body of Qi is completely washed of impurities, strengthened and then becomes free. The path of achievement is by cleansing the Qi in all your tissues through various exercises. You can do this through pranayama exercises and then internal energy practices, for this is the entire purpose of those exercises. The ultimate prize is reserved to those who persevere with practice to the end.

Subtle body, Causal body, Supra-Causal body and Immanence body can all be attained through this process. Then one will have the deva eyes, wisdom eyes, dharma eyes and Buddha eyes mentioned in the *Diamond Sutra* since they belong to the deva body that is the subtle body, Wisdom body that is the Causal body, Dharma (Clear Light) body that is the Supra-Causal body, and Buddha body of complete enlightenment that is the Immanence body. You can simultaneously possess all these bodies threaded together as if on a single chain where each lower body is linked to a higher body attainment. This is the *sambhogakaya* achievement of which Buddhism speaks, and is symbolized by the *Vishvarupa* body within Hinduism.

The human body's energetic nature internally contains the potential of the subtle body composed of Qi. The subtle body contains within itself the potential of the Casual body composed of Shen. The Causal body contains within itself the potential of the Supra-Causal body composed of Later Heavenly energy. The Supra-Causal body contains within itself the potential of the Immanence body composed of Primordial Heavenly energy. This final body is the Great Golden Arhat's Buddha of Perfect and Complete Enlightenment, the transcendental stage of No More Learning in Buddhism.

All these higher bodies are released from within their preceding lower ones only through the process of cultivation. Martial arts and yoga are two highly expeditious routes that can lead to this type of attainment, which then makes one an Arhat, *jnani* or Immortal, but such an achievement is possible only if you add internal energy practices to your *wai-gong* muscle practices. If you just train your muscles, then your efforts will be fruitless.

The deficiencies of ordinary muscle training become apparent when people get older and become weak. The Chinese have a relevant saying, "Training in physical techniques without training your Qi, it is all in vain when one becomes old." Therefore you have to start training your Qi *now*.

Each of the higher bodies has its own special powers and abilities that make possible some of the legendary feats you sometimes hear of in yoga and the martial arts. However, you will not be able to attain them if you do not train in virtue and cultivate your internal energy.

Conceit, gluttony, pleasure, and arrogance are the vices of Arjuna, Bhima, Nakula, and Sahadeva, the enlightened martial heroes of the *Mahabharata* who achieved these higher attainments. Enlightened they became, but vices they still possessed. Therefore, because you will always carry faults with you, despite enlightenment, think deeply on how to control yourself so that you do not harm people with the martial skills and powers you train to develop.

In the *Ramayana,* arrogance, anger, envy, rudeness, lust, greed, insecurity, impatience, and domineering are nine of the ten heads of the enlightened demon Lord Ravanna, who was an ordinary man who cultivated to achieve the higher transcendental body attainments. Only one of his heads was filled with wisdom and reverence. Thus the Chinese have a saying, "Your Tao might be one foot tall, but your capability for evil might be ten feet high. When your Tao reaches ten feet tall, evil tendencies might still be above your head."

In cultivating yoga and the martial arts, you must always be cultivating your character. Hatred, anger, resentment, annoyance and vexation, if you are unable to transform and remove them, once touched they stir into existence. If people are unable to subdue them it is had to be a good person.

In the *Surangama Sutra,* it is said that some who attain enlightenment take refuge in the devaloka heavens of the Desire Realm, and then surround themselves with treasure and beautiful women. The proclivity to greed, sensual indulgence and attachment is never cut off. Money, power, status, sex, fame, entertainment and advantage even tempt sages.

With these warnings you should always remember that once you attain a higher body, your personality characteristics such as your faults will always be carried along with you. Only a devotion to humility, open-mindedness, concern for others, and a constant drive for self-perfection that depends on the mirror of self-correction, can help you wipe away your stains and save you from using your power to aggress upon others.

Yogis and martial artists therefore stress the cultivation of a peaceful mind of clarity that is free from the taints of anger, malevolence, ill will, greed and attachment to sensual indulgences. When practiced steadfastly admirable traits such as truthfulness, fairness, a constant drive for self-improvement, respect for others and courtesy can become intrinsic to your character. Practitioners must always work to develop their character (such as cultivating a respectful demeanor and enhancing their sense of ethics and morality) while striving to unify their mind, body and technique with their vital energy. The celestial way is through humility, charity and compassion along with noble consummate conduct that takes us far above our animal nature.

Elegance, grace and nobility in thought, expression and movement, are these not worthy of an aspiration and commitment to self-development work? Should we not infuse a spiritual sense of self-perfection into the training methods for achieving mind-body mastery? Should we not work hard at self-cultivation so that our bodies can follow our wills gracefully, and so that we truly achieve mind-body unity?

Yoga and the martial arts are pathways to self-perfection, and in their training routines proper human conduct should be emphasized. Ultimately we must strive to improve our personality, character, morality and behavior. If during training we strive to elevate the human spirit, this will contribute to social prosperity and harmony, and ultimately benefit the world.

The virtue training methods of Yuan Liao-Fan and Benjamin Franklin, who both established personal codes of conduct as standards for their behavior, are part of the Confucian "Great Learning" that is necessary in life. The Golden Rule in living is doing for others what you would want done for yourself, and not treating others in ways you wouldn't want to be treated. Without accumulating such merit, and without changing one's personality, no one ultimately succeeds in attaining the heavenly reward.

When vital energy arises inside you, the body floods with power. At that time it becomes difficult to control yourself and resist the temptation of indulgences. The passions such as the desires for sex or food as well as pride or the abuse or criticism of others rise commensurately with your power status. The appetites never end for those who cannot control their mind. Attitudes and tendencies can be slowly changed over time, but until then the problem is how to control the emotional mind and automatic unwholesome reactions.

In his apparitional body, Samantabhadra therefore appears to others riding atop a white six-tusked elephant. The elephant's head represents his genitals, while the six tusks represent the six nerves protruding from his sacrum. Therefore Samantabhadra's riding vehicle, the white elephant of great power, simply represents his hips and pelvis that contain a purified potential of great power that isn't devoted to sexual activity or other passions.

Samantabhadra always travels on his elephant, which symbolizes his hips. His elephant is white in color because he has purified his vital energy as well as his carnal appetites, aggressive tendencies and lust for power. In control of his Qi and washed of aggressive tendencies, Samantabhadra rides about using his energy to perform great deeds to help others. He displays his great cultivation attainment and his vows through the symbol of his six-tusked white elephant.

This is the goal of yoga and the martial arts – purification of your Qi along with control of your mind, behavior and power, and devotion to the good. The training pathways of yoga and the martial arts never deviate from these objectives.

14

REPLACING INEFFICIENT
MENTAL PATTERNS

Neijia involves moving your Qi with your mind, opening up your Qi channels, and then igniting a *kundalini* process so that your Qi circulation proceeds automatically in the most optimal manner. At first you learn to use your will to move your Qi, which means using coarse or heavy thoughts when leading your Qi. Next you use your intent, which is a more refined type of thought. The final accomplishment is where your Qi will naturally follow your thoughts and match with your movements without need of any mental pressure at all. For *neijia*, which is *nei-gong*, you progressively train the connection between your thoughts and your Qi until you create optimal mental patterns for the process, and pathways of Qi circulation are cleared within your body.

Frequent, intensive, high-quality practice is the path forward. You must spend time intensively working to improve your skills. Through deep deliberate practice you want to reach a stage where you move without intent according to learned patterns that have become automatic, and your Qi flows perfectly as well. This is the pathway to flow and martial excellence.

Training in martial arts entails moving past your physical and inner barriers. Putting aside the topic of internal energy, sometimes it is your mind that restrains you rather than the capabilities of your body or its energy. We are all helped or hampered by our inner psychological disposition, attitudes, views and patterning. Emotions, for instance, can raise your spirit or hamper the display of your abilities. Mental barriers such as limiting beliefs, in particular, are a type of imprisonment that can prevent you from your highest possible achievements. They can even suppress the full expression of your Qi during a physical engagement. Hence, maintaining (rather than eliminating or retraining) suboptimal mental patterns is to your great detriment. Like bad habits, they must be eliminated.

As an example, by building up a wall of belief that you can't do something, you freeze your mental and physical progress. You put an artificial limit on your capabilities by believing you just cannot accomplish something that you might be able to achieve. You must always have the confidence that talent can be learned, and progress comes from incremental improvements. In the martial arts, if you adopt the principles that you are always open to change and that talent can be learned through deep deliberate practice, you just have to persevere with practice in order to reach a higher level of attainment even if you don't think it possible. If you can put aside any internal resistance you feel when confronted by challenges and "just do it," then your Qi will flow better and your natural abilities will come out.

Thoughts can bind your Qi flow, emotions can bind your Qi flow, beliefs can bind your Qi flow, mental perspectives can bind your Qi flow, habit energies can bind your Qi flow, and your personality can bind your Qi flow. They must all be transformed if you seek the highest levels of yoga and martial arts. Mental patterns can inhibit both your physical performance and Qi circulation so you must learn how to reprogram bad patterns, or free yourself from patterns entirely by replacing them with a mental fluidity that makes you formless, unfathomable, unpredictable as to your reactions and movements.

In yoga and the martial arts you normally proceed from physical muscular and movement development to Qi development. You first learn optimal physical patterns and afterwards internal energy movements. You initially learn set forms for a certain way of doing things, and gradually progress to being able to innovate separate from these patterns.

You also start with static physical drills, but if you want to improve your competitive abilities you must go beyond precision in the small details of routine movements. You must incrementally increase the level of chaos and challenge in your training practice, and then you can dramatically progress beyond the standard patterns you have learned. If you train relentlessly in pressure conditions or in strange environmental conditions beyond your normal comfort zone, and if you acclimate yourself to stress, surprise and shock, then this type of training will set you apart from your peers.

The best athletes in sports have typically gone past others due to their training. They train beyond their comfort zone in unstructured environments that added stressors beyond those of normal training practices. They continuously take the extra step in competitive training. They continually make practice more challenging so that they keep getting better at their skills and continually go beyond their thresholds. They recognize that if their performance was totally dependent on perfect conditions then they might fail if they encountered real life unexpected surprises. Hence, they undergo drills that facilitate improvisational responses, which in turn foster the skills of adaptation and innovation.

You are seeking to flow – to be able to move appropriately, skillfully, effortlessly, and with fluidity in response to situations. This requires you to adapt to situations, always remain focused and to ignore distractions. When in flow it should be just you and the task at hand where you are completely in the present.

Martial arts are a great training vehicle for attaining flow since they often involve extreme consequences such as life or death. Thus they require incredible focus and attention. "In flow" your concentration must be so involved with your focus that nothing else matters. In combat situations you must pay continuous attention to small signals, so you must remain in control of your attention despite unexpected events, errors, distractions, internal resistance or fear. This is where your mental habits and mental conditioning come into play.

The ability to avoid distractions in the mind and stay focused on what is important is what keeps you in flow. This requires calm and focus – a calm and clear mind somewhat free of patterns (since you can never get rid of them entirely) that meditation can help you acquire since this opens up the Qi pathways in your brain and the rest of your body. The ability to flow and remain in flow necessitates being undistracted even by your emotions, so one of the vital components of training is that you need meditation practice to improve your level of continuous concentration along with an ability to control your emotional mind. Reciting mantras (a standard meditation practice) could give Sun Wu-Kong a headache because this symbolized the fact that mantra repetition was a way of controlling our monkey mind.

Consider that the highest levels of martial arts were developed in Buddhist or Taoist monasteries because this is where individuals were trained to control their mind. In fact, more than two-thirds of the Chinese martial arts originated in Islam, Buddhism and Taoism. The martial arts and yoga were used as training vehicles so that people could reach the spirit of their lives.

Since the martial arts are essentially fighting skills rather than just a form of personal development, for those interested in fighting you must learn how to overcome (not to become moved or distracted by) anger, fear and intimidation. Unlike the fearless Siegfried in Wagner's *The Ring of the Nibelung*, all of us have ingrained reaction patterns of fear and anxiety. Fear in particular creates a fog of thoughts that prevents our skills from unfolding. Martial artists in competition, for instance, are often seen grimacing, bracing, flinching, breathing incorrectly or resisting force. These patterns of fear reactivity are detriments and dysfunctions rather than advantages. Skills without confidence cannot achieve as much.

In fear the mind sabotages itself. Great performance instead requires emotional detachment and a tranquil mind where you do not add extraneous emotional interpretations onto situations. You are aware of your thoughts but detached enough from perfect entrainment (identification) with those thoughts so that better thoughts can arise within your mind that are outside the momentum of your thought-stream. You are aware of your thoughts but sufficiently detached from those thoughts so that you can flow freely from experience to experience without being chained to any one pattern or way of thinking, reacting and doing things.

Fear and anger will distort not only your clear perception of a situation but your abilities as well. Instead of becoming entrained with emotions or mental obsessions, you should always remain unruffled and within a state of flow (focus and concentration) regardless of the situation that confronts you. Thoughts about the past and future must fall away and you should become concentrated on your actions by becoming centered in the moment. Transcending your emotions and worries, you must ignore such thoughts and do what needs to be done.

For instance, when you are in a fight your spirit should be alert and sharp like an eagle, which is a state of focus and concentration that doesn't have excessive thinking, disturbances or distractions clouding your mind. Your best performance always occurs during immersion where you switch off expectations, desires and excessive thinking so that you can become one with your actions. This is also the flow state where with pure mindfulness you do things seemingly effortlessly.

You must therefore work at exercises that teach you how to control your emotional mind, which you can partially accomplish through meditation work, but you should also work hard at neural re-patterning where you cut off the old self and replace its responses with something higher. This especially applies to the emotions of fear and worry. You must work on mental conditioning and developing your character, which is why martial arts that stress moral and spiritual self-development are called the "yoga of courage and honor."

Visualization efforts, where you mentally rehearse yourself doing something at its optimal best, will also help you change your old mental states and develop the neural circuitry required for optimal performance.[19] On the other hand, being continually bound to inappropriate patterns will inhibit your performance and flow. For instance, there are some people who already have the right mindset, and they simply have to get their skills up to the point where those skills match their minds.

Therefore you must train in new patterns, including new emotional skills such as the ability to turn fear reactivity into excitement. One step towards transforming the old patterned self is by thinking and moving differently, which is the entire purpose of yoga and the martial arts. These two physical arts are activities of self-development that aim for both a new spirit along with new physical skills. If you are training correctly you should always come into practice in one state and leave in another state.

Yogis and martial artists continually train at different postures and movements in order to learn how to control their minds and bodies, improve their internal Qi flow and overwrite inefficient patterns. Better internal Qi flow itself will soften your personality, increase your wisdom capabilities, and improve your emotional control. Greater flexibility and agility will free you from being trapped by the present limitations of your body. There is a spirit within you who can recognize that all of this is meaningful and worthy of pursuit.

As another example, our natural confidence is typically covered over

---

[19] See *Visualization Power: How Scientists, Inventors, Businessmen, Artists, Athletes, Healers and Yogis Can Improve Their Powers of Visualization and Visual Thinking* and also, *Sport Visualization for the Elite Athlete* by Bill Bodri.

by personal patterns of fear reactivity. Confidence is naturally there just as peacefulness is already there, but they are covered over. Over time many of us have gradually developed patterns of tension that have become ingrained habits, such as flinching or grimacing, avoidance or stonewalling. However, you can unlearn these patterns just as you can retrain any pre-performance anxiety to become excitement. One of the keys is breathing, for fast and shallow breathing allows stress to block our fighting skills. The practice of pranayama is therefore warranted to help us change our dispositions. For states of anxiety elite soldiers are trained to ignore their fear and become occupied in simply doing whatever needs to be done.

Whenever you break away from unnatural or inefficient mental patterns your Qi will begin to flow more freely and fully within your body, your vitality will rise extraordinarily, and you will feel more alive. This is because you will more closely approximate being your true natural self rather than some artificial self that has adopted all sorts of contrived restrictions. All of us have adopted some degree of unnatural falsity derived from prior influences and conditionings that have shaped us away from a better nature. We must learn to identify with our true inner self rather than a false persona that society wants us to be, and of course we must strive to elevate and ennoble that "inner me."

While the mental awareness and detachment practiced during meditation are one way to reduce the chances that old mental patterns will continually arise to seize and dominate your thought-stream of consciousness, it is the repetition of optimal ways of thinking and doing that will create new neural circuits to replace bad prior conditioning. Mentally rehearsing great performances through visualization practice will especially help you to internally secure and stabilize in your brain any desired patterns that you want to become your standard default patterns.

A high target is to become perfectly spontaneous and ultimately free of (selecting) all learned patterns, nevertheless you must initially train to learn excellent patterns (forms and *asanas*) so that you can develop automatic skills. This is the only way for great behaviors to become natural. You have to practice the best patterns, install those patterns within your consciousness, and then reach the stage where the best pattern for a situation is automatically selected without thinking. You have to master your skills so completely that you become one with those talents.

The thinking mind slows reaction time in the martial arts, and can be a detriment at a time of threat stimulus. Hence, when presented by a threat, immediately choosing the appropriate pattern within your brain without thinking is the most optimal way of responding, and constitutes flow. Practice teaches you how to reduce your reaction time to threats, and training conditions you to taking the appropriate automatic responses without hesitation.

Becoming spontaneous with flowing movements does not mean you should never use thoughts because at times careful strategy, planning and intent are needed, which are special mental functions of deliberate consideration. While you need to install optimal movement and reaction patterns within your memory, you must also always continue studying and learning to master higher levels of understanding and consideration so that excellent deliberation skills are always ready on call.

However, once again there is a model of perfection all admire that goes beyond the ordinary thought processes of deliberate thinking. It comes from the *Zhuangzi* wherein there is the story of Prince Wen-hui's cook, Ting, who engages in his work of cutting up an oxen while in flow, and his skill significantly impresses his lord. Prince Wen-hui's commends Ting on his skill whereupon the cook replies, "What I care about is the Way, which goes beyond skill. When I first began cutting up oxen, all I could see was the ox itself. After three years I no longer saw the whole ox. And now, I go at it by spirit and don't look with my eyes. Perception and understanding have come to a stop and spirit moves where it wants." Can we train in the martial arts to reach such a level? Many aspire to just this stage of internal mastery.

The main point is that even if you learn countless external physical skills and internal energy practices, the patterns of your mind can ultimately inhibit your Qi flow and sabotage your martial arts. To reach the upper levels of training, you have to transcend your mental barriers, your primal programming and eliminate layers of inappropriate patterning that you have developed over time. You must always remain a student open to change and learning despite any conditioning you have already adopted.

You may have to undertake a large variety of exercises to retrain your learned conditioning. After all, you must transform your prior mental behavioral traits that bias your reactions and warp your inner Qi flow. You must replace them with more optimal patterns instead. There is always a higher optimal for each level of skill development, and to incrementally reach towards those higher levels is always a great adventure. Incremental improvement will always bring you a great distance.

In addition to mental flexibility and the desire for self-improvement, perhaps the most important attitude to learn is that of humility. This is of utmost importance. As the saying runs, "The taller the bamboo grows, the lower it bows." As much as you achieve, there is always someone better than you at whatever level you reach. You must always then be a student for there is always more to learn and practice.

Humility will preserve you because in being humble you will avoid bragging, showing off and inviting challenges that may injure your body permanently. Humility also emboldens people to aspire to their highest potential and enables them to make the incremental improvements necessary to progress toward that potential. The highest fighting strategy is not fighting at all, and humility helps you avoid the trap of unnecessary violence.

15
HIGHEST LEVEL STRATEGY

Remember these levels on the road to great success. Jing stands for cultivating your body through diet and exercise. Qi stands for cultivating your inner vital energy and power through inner energy exercises of accumulation and circulation. Shen stands for cultivating your mind and cognitive powers such as thinking, imagining, and strategizing as well as wisdom, attitudes and perspectives. Later Heavenly Qi stands for cultivating your will power, perseverance and personal purposes (vows, pledges, objectives, goals and aspirations).

Nobility and irreproachable conduct are the greatest human virtues. To perform altruistic deeds of kindness and compassion achieves the greatest merit. To win respect, wisdom, kindness and morality are king. By taming the emotions and purifying aggressive tendencies we transcend our animal nature and enter the road of divinization.

What objective beyond divinization is more worthy of your time and effort? Devote yourself to self-development efforts rather than overt aggression. Self-development efforts that have meaning bear far more fruit than the endless treadmill of forever pursuing pleasant sensations or excitement. Enter the road of divinization to achieve the perfected body and mind, unified as one, where flow is your natural state of existence. Learn to control your thoughts, moods, body, internal energy and actions, and live your life to the fullest in happiness. Purify your aggressive energies by directing them into energies of transformation for this achievement. Devote your energies to building a better you, and to creating a better tomorrow with peace and prosperity for all.

Fighting is about winning over an opponent, but finding a way to control him without fighting is higher. Can you find a way to move him without touching him? The gateway is through influencing his mind. Another gateway is by altering circumstances. If you apply the various philosophies of martial arts when facing challenges you can learn to control yourself and ultimately control your opponents with little effort. The inherent idea within martial arts is that a small person who knows the right techniques can beat a larger and more powerful opponent. Once you learn such knowledge, you can offer your wisdom to your nation. Perhaps you can even help the destiny of humanity itself.

If the prospect of conflict arises can you avoid it or conquer through another means? You can feign ignorance to avoid a conflict. You can dissuade fighting by showing your opponents they have no chance for victory. You can leave the arena to avoid an unnecessary fight, even if you would easily win. Using misdirection or persuasion you can redirect your opponent's objectives. On the other hand, if an opponent maneuvers you into an avoidable confrontation, they've already controlled you. Countless strategies are available to help you avoid the unpredictability of a violent altercation, all of which involve using your wisdom rather than your ego.

The best fight is the fight of no fight, which is no fighting at all. Yet the best defense is also to train in fighting because all men should be prepared to fight. This is like "Trust, but verify." One must train in martial abilities to dissuade possible aggression but also as preparation, which is why Miyamoto Musashi said, "The ultimate aim of martial arts is not having to use them." Individuals need to be able to defend themselves and their loved ones from harm should aggressive threats appear, and martial arts training can help individuals achieve the capability of physical dominance needed for protection. They can empower you with the ability to push back if a line is crossed. Thus they can help to establish an environment of mutual respect, peace and civility amongst potential opponents where civilized discourse is preferred over violence. Becoming strong dissuades fighting but once strong, you must not be foolishly tempted into fighting. Never undertake rash actions out of ignorance.

Nonetheless, if you must fight to protect yourself then do so with honor and morality. Avoid a prolonged conflict. Try to win quickly and with ease because you have trained and prepared. Be subtle to the point of formlessness so an opponent cannot guess your actions, and then you can quickly subdue him. Be unguessable, like the unfathomable nature of *Wuji*, for if you are not creative you will reveal a pattern to enemies. Attack out of nowhere, distract your opponents and mislead them to win. Adapt your tactics as necessary; as per the "water principle" of adaptability, the more flexibility and versatility you possess the more advantage you have. Smart martial artists try to control the attention of their opponents and thereby break their flow with distractions while maintaining their very own. Try to use such strategies in warfare.

The great Chinese general Cao Cao said anger clouds the mind and therefore prevents good judgment. You will not think clearly or derive good strategy by giving into malice and letting animalistic emotions (such as your temper) gain control of you. You must be able to perform calmly under stress, whereas anger will make hundreds of Qi meridians shake with unsteadiness. Sun Wu-Kong and Hanuman are both respected not just because of their martial prowess but because each transcended his animal tendencies, such as anger and violence, through the practices of personal self-cultivation.

If your Qi becomes agitated your emotional mind will become excited, but when emotions become steady then your mind will become peaceful. It is inner peace that gives you an advantage when facing opponents because calmness enables you to think clearly and make better judgments. When the mind is calm, millions of wandering thoughts are eliminated and clear concentration becomes possible. Luckily, you can train for wisdom, even-mindedness and levelheadedness through study and meditation practice. Sometimes winning a confrontation is simply a matter of wits and calm steadiness rather than strength, so never neglect the importance of studying strategy and developing your character.

To win you must therefore abandon the traits of enmity, animosity, hostility, ill will, and antagonism. Cultivate the mind of peacefulness instead. Only when your mind is calm and peaceful can you achieve clear perception, and then your judgments can be neutral and accurate. You need to use mind power to detect an opponent's weakest points and then strike at the right time. This calls for wisdom and clarity rather than simply brute force and aggression. Have you been training in personal stability, mental clarity and strategic thinking?

Remember that after a conflict, you must be able to make peace with your opponent through spiritual harmony, so strategy should be applied. Only then can you achieve a lasting peace that protects you. Isn't that the ultimate objective?

Remember that the better your strategy, the less warfare will cost and easier it will be to gain the advantage. The more strength or time you waste, the greater the chance that things will turn against you. The more brutal your methods, the more resistance you will encounter. If you disrupt your enemy's center of gravity, however, his ability to resist will collapse. If your enemy feels the burden of war with weight then the desire for peace will prevail. However, the more you try to impose a peace of your own making, the more resistance there will be. The more you demand of the defeated, the more he will try to reverse the outcome. The ultimate purpose is to attain a better peace, so always remember this ultimate objective.

War is not a game anyone should play - the loss of life is shameless and unforgiveable. Battle outcomes are unpredictable since the unexpected usually happens, and so success in warfare can never be guaranteed despite high emotions and positive expectations. The toil of generations can be destroyed in a single day through fighting, populations can become decimated, and yet stupid leaders are willing to flippantly risk such outcomes for their nation. When the legacy of a thousand generations is destroyed, who can say war is glorious or great?

True capability for fighting is showing your opponent they do not have a chance for victory and thereby avoiding a battle of destruction. One must tame the inclination for battle. Avoiding a conflict is the highest strategy of all. If there is to be a conflict, Sun Tzu said the acme of skill is to subdue the enemy without fighting.

Confucius's student Zi Gong used strategy and elegant persuasion to protect his state. Others have used diplomacy to avoid warfare. Fabius Maximus shadowed the enemy to avoid fighting and defeat. Countless examples of alternatives to war are available. Instead of using physical force to attack or defend yourself, can you merely redirect your opponent's movements to your advantage as in *taijiquan*? Can you break an opponent's resistance without attack? A hundred methods are superior to the losses suffered by fighting.

If you can avoid a fight, this is the highest level of fighting. In avoiding a war you have won the war. To yield at times or retreat is not necessarily losing. Achieving your objectives without combat – that is the highest martial strategy.

If you absolutely must fight, Sun Tzu emphasized deception and surprise. Miyamoto Musashi emphasized psychological tricks to unbalance the enemy. Sun Bin advised tiring out the enemy and then attacking him unexpectedly. Clausewitz emphasized concentrating force at a decisive place and time. Napoleon emphasized taking the offensive. Genghis Khan emphasized maneuverability. John Boyd emphasized making speedy adaptive responses. Mahan emphasized sea power. The Romans were skillful in employing sieges to cut off enemy supplies. Kuan Tzu emphasized conquering others through economics rather than fighting, and Rothschild manipulated the financial markets for conquest. Use the strategy best appropriate for the situation at hand.

To avoid martial confrontations by promoting joint harmony, peace and prosperity is the best strategy of all. Pacify your state internally through wise polices, and neighbors through trade and friendship. Conquer your aggressive tendencies, but become strong so that your opponents pause with restraint. Harmonize your internal energy to reduce aggressive tendencies but become secure in your ability to project power to protect yourself and others. Use wisdom and effort to make yourself stronger and your country stronger, and dissuade aggressive attacks by others through a strength that dissuades conflict. This is the way to harmonize the world without war.

In Sattva Yuga, devas gave people good thoughts and good deeds abounded. In Kali Yuga, they train by abandoning discipline and giving people negative temptations. You must choose whether to recreate Sattva Yuga or not in your life, in your community and in your nation. You either follow the crowd and adopt its baser notions, or become an independent individual of principle who with morality and wisdom thinks for himself. You should try to elevate both yourself and your country to whatever is highest rather than remain a Sheeple who constantly bends to society's lowest programming.

The five training methods are to train the body, train the breathing, train the mind, train the Qi and train the spirit (to shine peacefully). The mind is the most important because it controls the whole situation, so train your mind. Remember that your Qi follows your mind in harmony with your breathing. Therefore you must train these three and match them with your movements and spirit.

If you work on developing your mind you can boost physical martial art skills and yogic abilities. To reach a high level of skills, your mind must become calm and peaceful. This absolutely requires training in meditation and concentration practice so that calmness becomes part of your personality. Many individuals train all these factors and then become unrivaled in excellence. Practice hard with diligence and discipline and see what kind of potential you can reach.

APPENDIX
SAMPLE TYPES OF "EMPTINESS MEDITATION"

Martial artists and yogis are advised to practice meditation. Here is one of the most comprehensive lists for various types of "emptiness meditations" you can practice:

- Set your mind on the highest ether of consciousness that is above all thought-constructs. Let go of thoughts and remain there.

- You should concentrate intensely on the idea that this universe is totally an ephemeral, effervescent illusion populated by transparent images, ungraspable like mirages that lack inherent existence. Let your mind become like that empty (void) substrate in which they appear.

- Go to an empty field or plane and stare into space. Take no notice of the clouds in the sky but become the space itself, infinitely everywhere. Let go of everything and become space. Rest in that state ignoring (staying detached from) any thoughts that arise without suppressing them. Let them appear with clear knowing but don't attach to them since you are bodiless and limitless like space.

- Imagine that, like a fish, you are swimming in an infinite ocean of pure consciousness without any obstructions whatsoever. Now, maintaining that imagination, imagine that you lose your fish body and you are a bodiless observer in a universe of pure consciousness.

- Imagine you are a pot of water immersed in water. Next, imagine what it is like if the pot breaks and there is water both inside of you and outside of you, and then just one water in all. Now imagine as if you are a pot of air resting in space, and similarly the pot disintegrates. What are you like? Be that. Rest there.

• Imagine that you are a point of light within an ocean of infinite light. Let go and become nothing. Next, try to feel that you are that ocean of light, which has no borders or form. Make that point of light merge in the infinite ocean of light.

In some of these approaches you try to feel that you or your consciousness becomes infinite, and in others you try to feel that you are part of the infinite by taking an infinitude as the subject of your consciousness and thinking of yourself as a manifestation of that infinite. You must try each method to see what works best for you. When you find that your internal energy stirs because of practicing some technique, that is a good sign of progress.

The *Vijnana Bhairava*, which is a how-to meditation book from the tradition of Kashmir Shaivism, contains instructions for practicing over one hundred different types of meditations. Several of these meditation practices embody different roads for cultivating mental emptiness. In order to avoid getting into a rut where you cling to the realm of emptiness that you are generating within your mind as an image, I suggest you devote yourself to a new one each week and cycle through them on a yearly basis. This is one of the quickest ways to develop meditation progress.

Some other emptiness meditation methods are as follows:

• Visualize the Qi of your body arising from your root chakra (your pelvis) as getting subtler and subtler until at last it dissolves into emptiness and remains there. Let your mind become empty like the final dissolution state of that Qi.

- Fill the center of your brain with Qi (visualize it coming into the brain from the spine, or draw it into the top of the head from the cosmos, or imagine it being a projection into your head from a spiritual master, etc.) and keep letting go of any thought-constructs. Let your mind become un-minded. Let your thoughts go to the state of being unmanifest. Your consciousness will eventually become empty if you continue letting go of whatever arises within your mind after first bringing Qi into your head.

- Use breathing to calm your thoughts and touch mental emptiness. You must first inhale air through your nose into your lungs, and then exhale slowly from your mouth to empty your lungs as if you are letting go of everything. Your exhalation should last about twice as long as the length of your inhalation, and you should let go of all your mental pressures and tensions upon those exhalations. Try inhaling for a count of four and then exhaling for a count of eight, and continue doing this several times in a row. When exhaling, always remember to let go as if you are finally releasing a big burden off your shoulders, and it is as if "now life is perfect." Each time you exhale make a silent sound of "Ahhh" as if you are so happy to let go of everything in the world and release all your problems and pressures. Eventually you will reach a point where you feel like you have let go of everything, your body feels comfortable inside, and your mind should now be quiet and a bit peaceful.

- Meditate by locating your consciousness in your heart, and hold your thoughts and energy there so that discursive thinking disappears. Upon the disappearance of your thought-stream stay absorbed in that emptiness. Alternatively, restrain your mental activities in the heart chakra (or on a flame that appears therein) and try to cultivate an empty mental state therein that eventually envelops your body.

- Recite the sound "Ohm" or "Aum" and observe the void of emptiness at the end of the protracted syllable. Doing this each time, you will eventually attain an experience of mental emptiness. For some people "Ohm" works better than "Aum," so you must try both sounds to see which works best for you.

- Imagine that you are empty space in all directions simultaneously without any thought-constructs, so you are emptiness surrounded by emptiness all around you. Imagine being the spatial vacuity in all directions around you and rest your mind in that state. If anything arises, let it arise within you because you are just infinite emptiness, bodiless, boundless and limitless like space. Being space you cannot grasp anything so just let go of whatever arises within your mind.

- Imagine there is endless space above your head, below your feet and within your heart. Rest your mind in that visage of empty space without holding onto any thoughts that arise. Simultaneously imagine that the upper part of your body is void and the lower half of your body is void. In your consciousness there is nothing, in both halves of your body is nothing, and in everything everywhere there is nothing. Rest in that mental realization.

- Contemplate that the constituents of your body (such as the bones, flesh, etc.) are pervaded with mere vacuity (emptiness). Imagine that they are empty inside. In other words, imagine that there is nothing inside your body's components. In time, the contemplation of having empty body parts will become steady and you can then extend the idea of emptiness to resting your mind in empty space as well.

- Contemplate that the skin of your body is like an outer wall and that there is nothing inside it but empty space. After you imagine that the body becomes like an empty sack, imagine that your mind becomes limitless and infinite in all spatial directions. All things you experience appear within this infinite spaciousness, but you know them without attaching to them because nothing is you - you are just the empty space that cannot attach to anything. Rest your mind in empty space like that.

- Bring your mind and your senses into the interior space of your heart – the ether or voidness of the heart - and exclude everything else from consciousness.

- Penetrate all parts of your body by consciousness, feeling all the parts of your body as a unified wholeness of soft energy, and then bring your mind of thoughts into the brain and let go of it so that it turns into emptiness.

- Imagine that the whole universe is successively dissolved from a gross state into a subtle state, from a subtle state into emptiness, and then from emptiness into an even more transcendental, formless, supreme state that lacks any attributes or distinctions. Allow your mind to be dissolved away into pure empty consciousness the same way and then let it become the emptiness of unmanifestation. This is called the technique of *sadadhva* where you trace the entire universe back to its source.

- You should concentrate intensely on the idea that this universe is totally void, without substance, completely empty. Imagine that it is a nothing for even atoms are empty space. In that emptiness (void) let your mind become absorbed.

- You should cast your eyes in the empty space inside a jar or any other empty object while leaving aside the enclosing partitions. Let your mind get absorbed in that empty space, and next imagine that your mind becomes absorbed in a total void of infinite emptiness. Let yourself become identified with that infinite voidness.

- Cast your gaze on a region in which there are no trees, such as going to a mountain plateau or high wall and looking into the empty sky. Let your mental state become like the empty sky you observe. Let thought-fullness become thought-lessness as you try to merge with that empty space. Let your thoughts dissolve as you become the empty space. Cast aside your body and ignore the fluctuations of your mind as you become the empty space you see.

- Contemplate with an unwavering mind that your whole body and the entire universe simultaneously are the nature of consciousness. Since your consciousness is what sees everything as pictures, then anything you are seeing is only consciousness (only images within your consciousness). Therefore the body you normally take yourself to be and the universe you see are just mental images of consciousness-only. Stay in that realization that the "you" ("I") that you take yourself to be is therefore ultimately pure consciousness that is pure and empty without perturbations like space.

- Contemplate that your whole body and the universe simultaneously are in their totality filled with bliss. After being fully permeated and saturated with this bliss, let go of all consciousness and let the mind rest in this blissful feeling without thinking. Don't even cling to the bliss but just let yourself be infinite bliss.

- Concentrate on your self in the form of a vast firmament, infinite and unlimited in any direction whatsoever.

- One should contemplate thus: "Within me the inner apparatus consisting of the mind does not ultimately exist for it is just brought about by a combination of atoms and energy in a particular structure that makes consciousness happen. In the absence of thought-constructs, I will be rid of all thought-constructs and will abide as pure emptiness." Try to become that ultimate state free of thoughts but without suppression.

- Sit in meditation and observe your mind and any desires or afflictions that spring up. When you observe a desire or affliction that springs up, put an end to it immediately. Don't let it function at all. Let your mind become absorbed in that very place from which it arose. In time your mind will become pure and clear like space.

- Consider, "When knowledge has not arisen in me, then what am I when in that condition?" Become absorbed in the reality of that emptiness lacking thoughts.

- After rejecting attachment to your body, you should with firm mind that has no consideration for anything else contemplate thus, "I am everywhere."

- Cast your gaze on an object, withdraw it and slowly eliminate the knowledge of that object along with the thought and impression of it so as to abide in non-knowing (without suppression) of thoughts.

- When a person perceives a particular object, absence is established regarding all other objects (including what you perceived just prior to this object). Contemplate on this vacuous absence with a mind free of all thought until you settle into a tranquil state.

• Fix your mind on the vast, limitless external space that is empty and without support. By prolonged concentration practice on becoming boundless external space, you will gradually acquire the capacity of mentally becoming like supportless, objectless, vacant space. Let your mind become absorbed in this experience.

• Towards whatever object the mind goes, one should remove it from there immediately by that very mind, and thus make your mind supportless by not allowing it to settle down anywhere. Just push your mind away from any point upon which it settles. Wherever the mind moves to, withdraw it to non-clinging emptiness. Do not attach to thoughts that arise within the mind. Let consciousness become perfectly free.

Visualization is often the precursor to a state of emptiness because when visualizing you condense your thoughts. During visualization, you concentrate on one image to eliminate all sorts of other wandering thoughts and thereby become mentally steady. Once the scattered thoughts are stopped, then you can visualize the Void or let go of the visualization to remain mentally empty and free like a void. That is called the state of emptiness, which is what we want to attain, and many meditation methods in the world have been derived to help us reach it. During that state, the Qi of the universe can more readily flow into you, and your own Yang Qi can more easily arise within you and start working on purifying the natural Qi circulatory routes within your body.

ABOUT THE AUTHOR

William Bodri is the author of a number of self-development books:

- Internal Martial Arts Nei-gong
- Sport Visualization for the Elite Athlete
- Nyasa Yoga
- Detox Cleanse Your Body Quickly and Completely
- Look Younger, Live Longer
- Quick, Fast, Done: Simple Time Management Secrets from Some of History's Greatest Leaders
- Move Forward: Powerful Strategies for Creating Better Outcomes in Life
- Arhat Yoga
- Bodhisattva Yoga
- Buddha Yoga
- Meditation Case Studies
- Culture, Country, City, Company, Person, Purpose, Passion, World
- Husbands and Wives Were Connected in the Past
- Super Investing: 5 Proven Methods for Beating the Market and Retiring Rich
- Breakthrough Strategies of Wall Street Traders

If interested solely in the martial arts and yoga then I would recommend also reading *Internal Martial Arts Nei-gong, Sport Visualization for the Elite Athlete, Nyasa Yoga*, and *Detox Cleanse Your Body Quickly and Completely*.

If interested in spiritual cultivation I would read *Arhat Yoga, Buddha Yoga, Bodhisattva Yoga, Nyasa Yoga* and *Meditation Case Studies*.

If interested in the optimal methods for mundane affairs I would recommend *Culture, Country, City, Company, Person, Purpose, Passion, World; Quick, Fast Done; Move Forward; Super Investing; Breakthrough Strategies of Wall Street Traders;* and *Husbands and Wives Were Connected in the Past*.

Printed in Great Britain
by Amazon

78417955R00108